Mental Health Education

PRINCIPLES IN
THE EFFECTIVE USE OF MATERIALS

Mental

Mental Health Materials Center
419 Park Avenue South
New York, N. Y. 10016
1969

Iealth Education

PRINCIPLES IN
THE EFFECTIVE USE OF MATERIALS

Nina Ridenour, Ph.D.

Publication of this work has been made possible
in part by Public Health Service grant MH 14899–03
from the National Institute of Mental Health.

Contents

Introduction

This book grew out of lectures given by Dr. Ridenour during a series of six one-week seminars on the effective use of materials in mental health education. To set the stage for the chapters that follow, I will describe these seminars briefly, beginning with an account of how they came into being.

All over the nation today, there are persons engaged in mental health education programs. Some work at it full-time: in state mental health, public health, and welfare agencies; in community mental health services; and in state and local mental health associations. Others work at it part-time, as one of their services to the public in the care-giving professions. Because the profession of "mental health educator" is a relatively new one, most of these persons lack a common professional training experience. Furthermore, most of these mental health educators function with little or no interchange of ideas with their counterparts in other parts of the country.

Recognizing that these people could use some help, the Mental Health Materials Center applied to the National Institute of Mental Health for a mental health project grant to demonstrate the usefulness of a series of regional seminar-workshops on mental health education, with the main focus on written materials since that had been the Center's primary interest. The objective was threefold:

1) To delineate some of the basic principles in the selection and production of mental health materials and the planning of mental health education programs.
2) To show how creative and imaginative uses of materials can strengthen a mental health program.
3) To guide participants in the improvement of their own skills in the effective use of materials.

After the grant was approved by the National Institute of Mental Health, the Center announced the seminars through mailings to mental health and public health departments throughout the country, selected prospective participants from the many candidates who applied, and arranged for six seminar-workshops to be held in university settings in different parts of the country, under the auspices of schools of public health or schools of medicine or state agencies. Each seminar was limited to twenty persons. (For a complete list of seminars, co-sponsors, and guest speakers please see Appendix.)

Seminar schedules were crowded. The daily program usually began with a lecture or presentation, followed by a period of group discussion, on some facet of the problems and processes in mental health education, accompanied by demonstrations of sample materials. Dr. Ridenour's lectures dealt primarily with principles and provided the basic foundation and framework for each of the six seminars. Presentations by other staff members of the Mental Health Materials Center and by guests supplied practical application of many of her points. Each seminar featured from two to as many as ten guest lecturers and panelists—persons selected for their competence and experience in mental health education and related fields.

In addition, throughout the week there were workshops in which an array of sample materials was analyzed for quality and potential use. One or two evenings were given over to demonstrations of the use of mental health plays and films. There were also a number of field trips to see various mental health education programs in action.

Prior to the seminars, each participant was sent four books as required reading:

Caplan, Gerald. *Principles of Preventive Psychiatry.* New York: Basic Books, 1964.

Joint Commission on Mental Illness and Health. *Action for Mental Health.* New York: Basic Books, 1961.

Cornell Conference Report. *Mental Health Education: A Critique.* Philadelphia: Pennsylvania Mental Health, 1960.

Ridenour, Nina. *Mental Health in the United States: A Fifty-Year History.* Cambridge: Harvard University Press, 1961.

They were also given a sheaf of representative program materials, good and bad, to be studied for later discussion in the workshop sessions. In addition, other relevant literature was described and education techniques were demonstrated by the staff and guests. Thus the group gradually acquired a considerable background in the theory and practice of using materials in mental health education.

The participants represented a wide range of disciplines, including medicine, public health, social work, psychiatry, psychology, nursing, journalism, and public relations. More than half were on the staff of a state mental health authority or one of its local units. Several participants were from voluntary mental health organizations. All were active in program planning in mental health, and most of them carried specific responsibility for mental health education. Although their professional backgrounds varied widely, as did the programs of their respective agencies, most of them had had at least some experience in community organization for mental health and were already familiar with a considerable range of materials. This book is therefore geared to the same type of audience— the "already oriented" in mental health education.

At the conclusion of the last four seminars, a questionnaire soliciting reactions was mailed to each participant within a week after the meetings. The overwhelmingly favorable response indicated that the program had been a valuable experience. Over and over again, participants reported that the seminars had given them confidence—*renewed* confidence in the potential and importance of mental health education and *greater* confidence in their own ability to evaluate mental health materials. Because so many of the correspondents singled out Dr. Ridenour's talks for special praise, the Mental Health Materials Center decided to publish them. Dr. Ridenour's statements carry the weight of many years of practical experience in developing closer working relationships between psychiatry and the allied service professions and in developing improved techniques in interpreting mental health concepts through printed materials, plays, and films. She herself adapted the lectures to book form and added considerable new material to Chapters V and VI. The result is a fascinating and highly readable work which should be useful and instructive to mental health educators—not only as a yardstick for present activities but as a beacon for future planning.

Alex Sareyan, Executive Director
Mental Health Materials Center

Mental Health Education

PRINCIPLES IN
THE EFFECTIVE USE OF MATERIALS

1

USING AND CHOOSING

THE CONCEPT "GOOD OF ITS KIND"

FIVE CRITERIA

SUBSTANCE

VALIDITY

BALANCE

AUTHORITY

INTEGRITY

Selection of Materials: Assessing the Content

"WHAT YOU SAY"

The subject here is "the skillful use of mental health materials." But of course before you use you have to choose. That is why it seems a good idea to start by taking a look at how one goes about assessing materials; first, assessing the content—what you say; and second, assessing the presentation—how you say it. The word assessing refers here to the process of passing judgment on a piece of material in order to decide whether you wish to use it and if so in what way.

USING AND CHOOSING

You might think that the importance of using good materials would be self-evident. But it is not. If it were, surely so much poor stuff would not be floating around. It is painful to see the quantities of mediocre and downright bad mental health materials constantly pouring off the presses, to say nothing of the rivers of stuff labeled mental health which is not that at all in any proper sense of the term.

Inevitably a lot of this poor and mediocre stuff lands on the shelves of the agencies involved in mental health education. For years some of us have been going around asking program people, "What materials do you use in your program?" and "How do you happen to be using this item or that item?" Time and again the answer is, "Because it's free"—or "Because it was there when I came,"—or "Because it was the only thing I happened to know about." One might call this "Selection by Default"—surely not a very sound basis for the selection process.

Choosing materials is not easy. Careful, thoughtful, knowledgeable selection of sound and appropriate materials is demanding. It takes time, money, experience, personnel, and resources. And yet what is more important in an education program than good materials? Good mental health education is not possible without good materials. Further, the effectiveness of mental health education is enhanced in direct relation to the sensitive, knowledgeable, creative use of materials.

The purpose of this book, therefore, is not to specify what materials to use, and still less how to run a program, but to set forth certain principles in the selection and use of materials likely to increase their effectiveness.

THE CONCEPT "GOOD OF ITS KIND"

"Good of its kind" is a concept that can be helpful when one is trying to make judgments about materials. The phrase is more or less self-explanatory. It means that you try to judge the item, whatever it is, *in terms of the purpose it is intended to serve.* This allows wide flexibility and yet implies some standard of excellence, comparable to judging a work of art for itself. It does not set up any pattern to which an item is expected to conform but serves as a framework for your own value judgments. One of the practical consequences of this approach is that you may suddenly see—become sensitive to —a new potential in an item, perhaps a new program angle you had not thought of before. Also if you conclude that the item is not "good of its kind," you may feel spurred to look further and try to find something that is up to your standards, instead of being willing to accept something inferior because it is the only thing you happen to know about at the moment.

Anyone who is thoughtfully and seriously trying to judge materials is usually trying to be as objective as he can. And yet true objectivity, in the sense in which it is used in the natural sciences, is rarely possible in mental health education. Indeed the entire concept of objectivity is now being articulately challenged by the new humanistic emphasis in psychology. It is the point of view here that one strives to validate subjective reactions and opinions against external measures if there *are* any external measures, but that subjective, intuitive judgments are also to be respected *if they are based on experience*—and please note the italics.

FIVE CRITERIA

The five criteria presented here represent an effort at amalgamating objective measures and subjective opinion. They do not make any pretense at rigid scientific objectivity, but neither do they give in to undisciplined subjectivity. Here are the principal qualities I myself like to look for when assessing material:

Substance
Validity
Balance
Authority
Integrity

If any item has these five qualities it is *probably* a pretty good piece of material. If it lacks any one of these to any marked degree, then it may be wise to take another look, although it does not follow that you will necessarily eliminate the item because you may have special reasons for using it despite its deficiencies.

SUBSTANCE

To satisfy the criterion of "Substance," first of all the item —pamphlet, leaflet, book, film, journal article, newspaper column, whatever it is—*must say something*. It is more than a little depressing to see how much so-called mental health material does not say anything—not anything at all. So first ask: Is this saying something, or is it just words put together? Is it saying something worth saying or is it simply yakkity-yak?

More than that, does the item *show evidence of being derived from an organized body of knowledge?* Mental health is a field in which practically everybody in the world considers himself an authority. And many people are writing "mental health material" who have no competence in the subject whatever. So you are justified in asking: Is this something just anybody could have written off the top of his head? Or does it reflect a sound background of knowledge? To satisfy the full criterion of "Substance" it must have some depth, some solid thought behind it, some claim to professionalism.

Futhermore, the material can be ever so *popular* in style, but *it must not be superficial*—an extremely important distinction. Something can be popular and still have depth. Because an item is intended for a large segment of the public or for readers of limited education or readers new to the subject matter, that does not mean it need be superficial. Sound, even profound ideas can be expressed in simple language; or superficial ideas can be dressed up in professional jargon. Popular means "for the people." Superficial means lacking in depth. There is not necessarily any connection between the two.

VALIDITY

The second criterion is "Validity"—and the derivation of the word is relevant here. It comes from words meaning "to be strong, to be worth" and according to the dictionary means something founded on truth or fact, capable of being supported or justified or defended. Psychologists and statisticians have given a technical twist to the words valid and validity which is not what is meant here. Valid, as used here, does not mean that the information under discussion is necessarily incontrovertible or "proven" or that it has even been shown to correlate with any external phenomena in any specified degree of probability. It means only that the information is "capable of being supported or justified" in the opinion of trained and experienced persons. Another way of saying this is that the item *must be as sound as our present state of knowledge* permits. This implies, further, that it must not contain any outright inaccuracies or distortions. Nor should it be open to a charge of known futility. These points require elaboration because, unfortunately, mental health education is full of inaccuracies and distortions and futilities, and these positively must be reduced if there is going to be any improvement in effectiveness.

For convenience the distorting qualities can be divided into several categories:

misrepresentations
—including out-and-out errors of fact
oversimplification
—both in advice-giving and in the interpretation of ideas
doubtful attributions
—attributing an effect to the wrong cause or jumping at
  conclusions on insufficient evidence
faulty perspective
—especially historical
known futility
—efforts at "education" previously shown to be futile.

Some of these keep going year after year, decade after decade, and truly they are cause for concern. The following are examples:

Misrepresentations. "Mental illness is increasing." That is an error of fact one sees stated repeatedly. You see it in press releases, in magazine and newspaper articles, in articles in professional journals; and particularly you see it in all kinds of publicity from mental health organizations, both voluntary and governmental. During the period this chapter was in preparation, it turned up in three places, not merely alluded to, but handled as the main point, the theme, of the item. One of these was a press release from an agency whose professional staff knows better; another was in a presumably well-researched article in one of the more sophisticated magazines; and the third was a brochure with headlines threatening catastrophe from the tidal wave of mental illness about to drown us all.

And yet every time anybody buckles down to a serious epidemiological study of the incidence and prevalence of mental illness—which is an extremely difficult thing to study—the conclusion is that mental illness is *not* increasing, if by mental illness is meant chiefly hospitalizable psychosis and that is usually what people do mean. You cannot state that mental illness is increasing in any given population unless you know a great deal about that population, including such details as previous resources for diagnosis and treatment, community attitudes, definition of terms, and many other factors. Mental illness is bad enough as it is. Let us not compound the tragedy by crying wolf about increase. There are better arguments for the need to "do something."

"Mental illness is just like physical illness"—that is another misrepresentation and an unfortunate one. It arose from the laudable motive of trying to change the public's attitude toward mental illness. But the constant repetition of this idea out of context has introduced a new distortion in the understanding of mental illness and has had unfortunate repercussions especially in the employment of mental patients and other types of rehabilitative effort. The correct statement should be something to the effect that "In some ways mental illness is like physical illness but in other ways it is very different." For the differences are important, and unless people are sensitive to these, many well-meaning efforts on behalf of the mentally ill are likely to fail.

But far more important than these two minor examples is another rampant misrepresentation: the rosy picture too often painted about the present status of the care of mental patients and progress in the entire mental health field. Magazines love to pick up a story of innovation in some one or a few situations and handle it as if radical and dramatic improvements were sweeping the country. Nor is the press the only guilty party. But the mental health millennium has not yet arrived nor is it even in sight. Conditions in some of our great mental hospitals *today* are still shocking beyond belief. The "Bedlams" have by no means all been eliminated in this country—and let none of us forget it. Misrepresentations are also rampant in some of the recent literature about the mentally retarded, extravagant claims that only arouse false and painful hopes among the people who care most and therefore have the most to lose when they discover that the claims are not justified.

Oversimplification. Mental health literature, especially of the popular type, is full of advice. "Talk it over." "Get psychiatric help." "Keep active." "Give reassurance." These are typical oversimplifications.

"Talk it over": yet how often talking it over with the wrong person can be a destructive experience for a disturbed person. "Get psychiatric help": a blanket recommendation—but how often it happens that psychiatric help is not available. "Keep active": this admonition is seen a lot these days, especially in connection with the aged. And yet common-sense observation tells us that it is normal for aging persons to be satisfied to restrict their activity, an observation that is being backed up by research. "Keep active" is far from being a panacea nor is it even wise counsel in some circumstances. "Give reassurance": how easy, and frequently how wrong. Research in therapy has shown that more often than usually realized patients are not "reassured" by "reassurance"; it is not what they want or what they need, and they are thrown off by it. More than that, research has also shown, for instance at the fronts during World War II, that the psychiatrists who had built their techniques on reassurance were less effective than those who used other forms of therapy. The point here is that glib, untested generalizations do not deserve the rubric "mental health education."

Another widespread form of oversimplification lies in trying to state complex ideas *too* simply. Often you can simplify with great effectiveness, and goodness knows much of the literature needs that. But you cannot simplify indefinitely. Eventually there comes a point where you had better say "This is a complicated idea and will lose substance if stated any more simply than this." You can go only so far. After that you are likely to get either a string of platitudes or meaningless generalizations. Dr. Alan Gregg has aptly commented on this point:

> We must face the intricate problem of simplification. I am rather inclined to think we do need some simplification. We have this immense public with varying degrees of capacity to interpret what is said. So perhaps it is all right to begin with some oversimplification. But it would not be very sensible to say "Now, the damned trouble with the compass that we use in navigation is that it needs simplification." I will go on the rocks if I simplify the compass by too many points. (10)

Doubtful attributions. This means attributing a given effect to the wrong cause, or what happens more often, attributing some very complex problem to a single cause. The whole mental health field is shot through with this type of erroneous thinking, where, for instance, the whole weight of an emotional disorder is "explained" in terms of a single past experience. And yet if there is anything we are clear about it is the prevalence of multiple causation. Examples are rife: delinquency "explained" by a single factor such as a drunken father or a reading disability or bad companions; behavior problems "explained" by a child's ordinal position—because he is the oldest child, or the youngest, or the middle child, or because he is an only child, or because he is one of a large family. There has been much too much of that in psychiatry and mental hygiene, and it is time we did more examining of loose attributions of this type.

Faulty perspective. This refers to lack of historical perspective, particularly to the assumption that later ideas and

ways of doing things are always better than earlier ones.
Sometimes this is due to inexperience; but sometimes it is due
to nothing more or less than trying to show that one is superior to one's predecessors. And it is consistent with the emphasis we place in our culture on the value of the new for its
own sake, the notion that whatever is the latest or the newest
is better than what went before—which "ain't necessarily so."
Good ideas, good work, are not a monopoly of the present gen-
eration, and denigration of the past often reflects little more
than ignorance of history plus a lack of humility that leaves a
bad taste in the mouth and is grossly misleading to the unori-
ented. More serious, lack of perspective on the past makes it
impossible to learn from the past, either from its failures or
its successes. Consequently we end up repeating the mistakes
of the past piled on top of a full set of mistakes of our own—
which is exactly what is happening right now as seen in some
of the totally unrealistic fantasies being advanced in connection with the care of the mentally ill and the prevention of
mental illness. More about that later.

Known futility. This section might have been headed "We
should have stood in bed." Here the main point is the utter
futility of exhortation when talking about feelings, the futility
of telling people how to feel—and what a lot of that is done
in the name of mental health. Be happy! Enjoy your work!
Love your child! Don't worry! Like people!

"Love your child": Suppose you have a committee which
decides that telling people to love their children is good mental
health education. So they recommend that you make a poster.
You order 50,000 copies and charge it to your education
budget. Granted, you may need posters, for you may have to
keep the name of your organization before the public in order
to survive. Granted also that children who are loved get along
better than children who are not loved. But it does not follow
that posters or car cards or handouts by the thousand are
going to make one single parent more loving toward one single
child. So please, let's not mislabel that type of admonition
"mental health." The same is true for most exhortations about
how to feel.

BALANCE

Balance is best described in terms of its opposite, imbalance. This means any excess, any extreme, any exaggeration, incomplete thought, half-truth, or significant omission, any statement that should be qualified and is not.

When dealing with complex ideas, as in mental health, there are many times when flat statements are not permissible, when you positively must qualify. "*Some* people do so and so," "*Sometimes* this or that . . . ," "In *some* circumstances . . . ," "It *may* be . . ." The dramatic writers hate these words. They call them "weasel words" and it is true they do tend to make writing ponderous. But better a little dullness than sweeping or inaccurate generalizations that cannot be supported.

One can get away with imbalance in the spoken word more easily than in the written word. That is, one does not have to be as careful in the spoken word. A speaker at a luncheon meeting, for instance, is trying to keep his audience from going to sleep so he tosses them a couple of startling statements, builds these up, and actually does succeed in being more interesting than if he weighed and qualified each statement. But when he puts the same speech in writing, it becomes apparent what he left out, where he has overstressed this point or that, and the whole speech may need revamping if it is not to be grossly out of balance. Imbalance is the omission of the "and then again on the other hand" which is so often necessary in mental health writing.

A fine example of good balance is the report of the Group for the Advancement of Psychiatry (GAP) on the psychiatric aspects of school desegregation (13). There the authors are dealing with an extremely complex subject, and each time they make a statement they examine it from all sides, look at it, weigh it, consider the alternatives, present the "and then again on the other hand." It isn't easy but it can be done.

A useful phrase is "in the round." Something written "in the round" presents all facets of a subject, has no significant omissions, is a full, complete handling of a subject, and above all is well balanced.

How can you make use of these criteria in your own writing or in the material you edit? Look at it sentence by sentence. Ask yourself: Do I really think this? Can I justify that? Have I gone too far in this direction? What is the alternative? Should I qualify this? Is that the whole story? What about this angle or that angle? Consciously striving for balance is a valuable aid to clear thinking, as well as to effective writing.

AUTHORITY

The authority behind a piece of material is a sort of negative safeguard. Good authority does not assure a good piece of material, and at times it happens that very bad materials are turned out under very good auspices and by able authorities. But naturally good authority increases the likelihood that a piece of material is good. If the item shows no evidence of any kind of authority behind it, then be suspicious. That does not mean it is bad. Nor does it mean don't use it. But do inspect it carefully.

Some of the details it is a good idea to look for when questioning authority are: Who is the author? Is he named? What is his training or specialization? Are any degrees indicated—M.D., Ph.D., M.S.W., R.N.? Is there an organization behind the item? Is it an organization qualified in the field under discussion? If the item comes from a commercial publisher is there other evidence of authority? Some of the pamphlets prepared for reading rack services are a case in point. If you examine them you will find first of all that the publisher is usually a name you never heard before. The author may be named but you are told nothing about him. No degree is given, no affiliation is mentioned, no sponsoring organization, no organization connected with the subject. So one begins to wonder, "Was this written just to sell? Or does it have real authority behind it?" It may turn out to be good but you will need to examine it twice as carefully as you would if you saw the kinds of names you have come to rely on.

If you see something from one of the federal agencies, such as the Children's Bureau or the National Institute of Mental Health, or the Public Health Service, that also does not completely assure its being a good piece but it does tell you there is authority behind it. The same is true of material coming from major voluntary organizations such as the National Association for Mental Health and the Child Study Association of America or from a university or graduate school; or from professional organizations such as the American Psychiatric Association, American Orthopsychiatric Association, Group for the Advancement of Psychiatry (GAP). None of these names are absolute guarantees of excellence, but at least they indicate that a reputable organization is behind the item.

The question of authority also comes up in connection with things put out by insurance companies and pharmaceutical houses, which are the two biggest suppliers of free materials. There is a kind of naïve assumption that if an organization is good and solid and dependable in its established field, then that will carry over into its mental health education. For instance, an insurance company may have a well-merited reputation for being a fine insurance company. If you are buying insurance you can do so confident that you are getting your money's worth. But if this company decides, as a form of institutional advertising, to start putting out pamphlets on mental health, does it follow that its mental health education will be as good as its insurance? It does not. You will be well advised to examine the material item by item for it may vary widely. Or it may vary from one period to another. For instance, there was a long period when one of the large insurance companies put out some of the best mental health stuff available. Then the head of the department retired, a new person came in, and the material became very superficial.

As mentioned before, much material gets used solely because it is free. Recently a mental health educator who had been assessing free materials announced a new discovery. "I see now," he exclaimed in amazement, "that I have just been *assuming* that those things were put out by responsible people." And then he went on to add that it had hit him practically with the force of conversion to realize that he dare not make such an assumption. Printing is no guarantee of soundness. Some material has no competence whatever behind it. So be alert.

INTEGRITY

"Integrity" is the most controversial and the hardest of the criteria to talk about. Integrity as used here means that the motivation behind a piece is what it purports to be; that there is no ulterior motive irrelevant to mental health education; and above all that there is no motive antithetical to sound principles of mental health education.

The most frequent of the ulterior motives is publicity, a topic on which there is much difference of opinion. Publicity is itself a completely legitimate motive, an entirely proper reason for producing certain types of material in mental health education. On that there can be no argument. We have to have things written specifically for publicity, for promotion, for fund-raising; things that interpret facts, ideas, concepts to the public; things that interpret the work of agencies, institutions, and organizations involved in mental health activity.

I think, though I cannot be sure—for one never can be positive about this kind of statement—that I wrote the first article that ever tried to show the importance of the public relations point of view in mental health education. That was back in the early 1940's when Madison Avenue techniques had only started to invade education and the now grossly misused word "communication" was just beginning to be bandied about. At that time it was quite a new idea that the people who came from the public relations field had something to teach those who were professionally trained in mental health. I was convinced then that they did and I am convinced now that they do. But meanwhile an awful lot of confusion has arisen between education on the one side and public relations on the other.

Most of the confusion comes about because the two fields have certain goals they share and certain goals they do not share. They are like two intersecting circles that have a certain area in common while each circle has an area it does not share with the other. The goal of publicity in its various forms is to get people to *do* what *you* want them to do: in advertising it is to get them to buy the product; in journalism it is to get them to buy the publication; in public relations it is to get them to support something, whether with voluntary contributions or tax dollars, or votes, or good-will, or specific action. In contrast a major goal of education is to get people *to understand.* Of course this is an oversimplified statement, because education is much more complex than that; also the goal of understanding implies the hope that if people understand, they will be more likely to act in appropriate ways than if they do not understand. The distinction here is between direct action as a primary goal and understanding as a primary goal. In public relations, a secondary goal may well be understanding but this is chiefly as a reinforcement for the primary or action goal. Insofar as both fields are involved in striving to develop understanding, they share common goals and supplement and support each other. The trouble arises when their goals conflict.

Since the goal of publicity is to get people to *do* something, it has learned a vast array of tricks to catch attention, to make an impression. From the point of view of education, some of these are acceptable and some are not. When attention-getting becomes an end in itself, and when the assumption is made that the end justifies the means (an assumption that is often made in public relations), then education is likely to suffer. If publicity goals and publicity techniques usurp education goals and education techniques, distortions creep in and integrity vanishes.

There are many kinds of attention-getting devices that are not acceptable in mental health education, not justifiable—attention-getting devices that destroy the integrity of educational materials. It is hard to talk about these because each one of them *may* be legitimate in its place, but each one is also subject to abuse. It is the exaggerations and excesses, the abuses and misuses, that cause trouble.

Among the abuses, one of the most regrettable is *appealing to people's needs and emotions when not justified*. Please double-underscore the "when not justified," for the mental health field is highly reprehensible in this direction. People's needs are vast. They long for happiness, for freedom from anxiety, for financial security, for professional success, for social success, for marital harmony, for peace of mind—the list goes on indefinitely. Much of the popular mental health literature *promises* such things to them if they will only read this pamphlet or memorize that list or this set of rules or see that film, or "get psychiatric help" or "talk it out with somebody." Look at all the pamphlets and all the sections or lists within pamphlets beginning "How to . . .": "How to be well adjusted," "How to be mentally healthy," and the like. Such promises are not justified! Maybe they were a little more so in earlier days, when our field was more naïve and just beginning to formulate exciting new concepts, and when we still thought we were going to change the world. But we are growing up now. We now know that reading a pamphlet is not going to save a marriage or reform a delinquent or prevent a mental breakdown. So let's not hold out that promise. No wonder there is loss of public confidence. No wonder mental health education comes in for opprobrium from the hardnosed school of scientists. Mental health education does have a great deal to say to people to help them understand themselves and others. It offers an important body of knowledge about human behavior. But when something starts out "How to . . . ," then beware. For it is almost always pandering to people's desire for specific answers, their wish to be told what to do, to have things made easy, and above all to their longings, healthy or neurotic, for the solution of personal problems. Sound, careful, thoughtful exposition of motivation, or any other type of good mental health education, is unlikely to start out "How to . . ."

An example of several of the points above is to be found in the widely distributed pamphlet *Seven Keys to a Happy Life* (16), by William C. Menninger, M.D. In this instance the material itself was notably sound and defensible, but when it was reprinted, distortion crept in—distortion that hurt the integrity of the entire piece.

Dr. Menninger's original title was *Seven Criteria for Emotional Maturity* and had been the title of a speech he had made at a State Mental Health Association. The speech went over so well and reprints were in such demand that it was decided to publish it as a pamphlet. The editor then changed Dr. Menninger's original title, *Seven Criteria for Emotional Maturity*, to *Seven Keys to a Happy Life*, and added headings, all in the imperative, as follows: Face Reality; Adapt to Change; Control Anxieties; Give of Yourself; Consider Others; Curb Hostility; Learn to Love. Nothing else was changed. The speech was an unusually full, rich, and altogether sound exegesis of Dr. Menninger's views on the subject of emotional health. In the body of the speech he had held out none of the promises implied by the new title, nor had he exhorted the listener in the manner of the new headings. True, both the words "criteria" and "maturity" can be objected to as being inappropriate in the title of a popular pamphlet. And one can understand why an editor might feel impelled to search for a title with more popular appeal. But that is exactly the point: to what extent should journalistic considerations be allowed to distort the message, even by implication? Once more: promising happiness is not mental health education.

Another regrettable example of exploiting people's longings is to dangle exaggerated expectations about what is going to be accomplished through "research," especially if the implication is that the glorious new day is just around the corner. As mentioned above, a lot of this is now being seen in connection with mental retardation where the subject is written up as if mental retardation were all but conquered, or as if there were no such thing as a mentally retarded person but only errors in diagnosis or social neglect or failure to recognize special gifts or misplacement in school or lack of a good job. Exaggerated promises are also being held out in connection with what can be accomplished through community psychiatry in the way of providing services "for all who need them," and dreams of eliminating all mental hospitals by "returning the patient to the community." To whatever degree such promises can be justified they should be interpreted to the public, *but they should not be exaggerated.*

Along with the hazards of "free" material prepared for advertising purposes without any sense of responsibility for soundness or accuracy, another subtle gimmick to be wary of is the "How we did it" approach. When an organization has actually done something different, or when it has a body of experience it genuinely wishes to share with associates, then a pamphlet or film about "how we did it" may be welcome. But when the true motivation is self-advertising, it will happen again and again that the substance is thin and unhelpful and that the material does not deserve to be called "mental health education." The same is true for some of the entertainment material masquerading as mental health where the entertainment goals pre-empt the education goals. Also the same thing happens in the tearjerkers and other appeals to emotionalism. Warm, human stories about the tragedies of mental illness and mental retardation can be used to advantage in interpretation. But drippy sentimentality rarely has a place in good education.

In summary, educational materials must maintain integrity. No extraneous motive such as the desire for publicity or wide distribution must be allowed to usurp the educational standards of honesty, accuracy, soundness. When goals conflict, and the true motivation for a piece is other than it purports, look out for subtle and insidious interferences.

2

THE AUDIENCE

    DEFINITION OF AUDIENCE

    APPROPRIATENESS FOR THE AUDIENCE
    FOR WHOM INTENDED

    INTERNAL CONSISTENCY
    WITH RESPECT TO THE AUDIENCE

THE QUALITY OF WRITING

    STYLE

    CLARITY

    TONE

    ORGANIZATION

MEDIUM AND FORMAT

Selection of Materials: Assessing the Presentation

"HOW YOU SAY IT"

For this chapter on "Presentation" it seems appropriate to begin with Lincoln's Gettysburg Address. Some readers may not have heard that it has been rewritten. You may find it instructive to compare the original and the revision. You will, of course, recall the older form: "Fourscore and seven years ago our forefathers brought forth on this continent a new nation, conceived in liberty and dedicated to the proposition . . ."—it is not necessary to cite more of it here because most readers will have memorized it in high school. Remember the ending "government of the people, by the people, for the people . . ." Please keep those cadences rolling in the back of your mind. Here's the rewrite.

"Eight and seven tenths decades ago the pioneer workers in this continental area implemented a new group based on an ideology of free boundaries and initial conditions of equality. We are now actively engaged in an over-all evaluation of conflicting factors in order to determine whether or not the life expectancy of this group or of any group operating under this state of conditions is significant. We are met in an area of maximum activity among the conflicting factors . . ." and so on. Then the closing lines: ". . . and we here resolve on a high ethical level that the deceased shall not have been annihilated without furthering the project, that this group shall implement a new source of unhampered activity and that political supervision composed of the integrated units, for the integrated units, and by the integrated units shall not perish from the superficial area of this planet." (Quoted with the permission of *Time* magazine.)

How is that for communication? Allowing for a bit of hyperbole, isn't that just about the way such a speech might appear in a professional journal today?

But before continuing with the subject of the quality of writing, it is necessary to consider the audience.

THE AUDIENCE

The way something is presented—"How You Say It"— should be shaped at least in part by the "To Whom." Who is the audience you are speaking to? Again and again the literature of the field sounds as if the writer had completely forgotten the audience for whom the material is intended. This might be called "The Case of the Forgotten Audience."

If the writer is not thinking about his readers, what then is he thinking about? Sometimes you can tell that he is concentrating exclusively on what *he* wishes to say, regardless of who is likely to read it. In other words he is writing—not to teach— but to express himself. This may be a good way to produce a work of art—poetry, essays, creative writing—but can it be depended upon to produce good educational material? I would say: only occasionally.

Sometimes the writer is not overly concerned with self-expression but totally absorbed in his subject—call it "subject orientation." That is, he is thinking only of covering all facets of his subject and is oblivious to all other aspects, such as how much is relevant under the circumstances. The result is that he will probably include a lot of extraneous material not appropriate for his readership, much of which could be omitted to advantage.

And then sometimes you can tell that the writer is thinking only of his peers. He talks in language *only* they could be expected to understand, with the result that the *only* people who can understand it are those who could have written it in the first place. Or even worse, he *assumes* his peers will understand him and thus makes no effort to make himself clear. (What a shock he would get if he gave a test of comprehension.)

Of course each of these three orientations has its place: self-expression in creative writing; subject-orientation in an encyclopedia article or a textbook; peer-orientation in a professional journal. But any one of these when carried to extreme is likely to interfere with the effectiveness of the material as education.

As an antidote to these faults there are three types of questions a writer or an editor would do well to keep in mind in order to keep the material oriented to the audience:

Definition of audience
Appropriateness for the audience for whom intended
Internal consistency with respect to the audience

DEFINITION OF AUDIENCE

Who is the audience? To *whom* are you speaking? Is the audience defined—not necessarily in words—but by implication? You don't have to say "This is intended for such and such an audience . . . ," but at least try not to leave a puzzle in the mind of the reader about whom the material is intended for. A reader, thinking of special groups or categories, should be able to say "Yes, this material is appropriate for that group," or "No, it is not appropriate." Examples of categories would be professionals, non-professionals, young people, people with limited education, people with or without training in some specific field, people with special types of experience, people already oriented, people already interested but not oriented.

Sometimes a writer starts out to write for one particular audience but gradually lets the audience grow in his own mind. That is the time to take warning. He will write something, say, for parents. Then it occurs to him that if he makes some reference to teachers, the material will do for teachers, too. Then he tosses in a reference to nurses or maybe group workers. Pretty soon he decides that this is "for all professional workers." So he ends up by announcing it as being intended "for all who are interested in children." This is the kiss of death.

Don't be afraid to *limit* the audience in your own mind. On that point Edith Stern, one of the best of our mental health writers, says firmly: "Don't try to reach everybody or you will reach nobody." There is much solid evidence to support this. Anything that is outstandingly good for a restricted audience invariably finds a variety of uses and ends up by reaching a larger audience than anticipated. The reverse is by no means always true. Instead, things that are aimed at too large an audience often end up by not really reaching any audience at all. The content becomes scattered, attenuated, inconsistent, often boring—in short, ineffective.

Another point for the writer to keep in mind is that the effectiveness of mental health education is enhanced when it is directed to "homogeneous, highly motivated groups." We are indebted to Dr. Loyd W. Rowland of the Louisiana Association for Mental Health for the phrase "homogeneous, highly motivated groups," a phrase and a concept that are extremely useful in developing materials and program.

"Homogeneous" as used here means homogeneous with respect to such factors as the interests of the audience, their problems, receptivity, felt need, the nature of their responses —any or all of these and other feelings and attitudes related to the subject of mental health. There is sometimes misunderstanding on this point. For instance, a neighborhood group, or a church group, or a PTA group in which the children cover a wide age range, though homogeneous in certain respects such as education or cultural background or community concerns, may not be homogeneous with respect to mental health problems or interests. Examples of homogeneous, highly motivated groups are parents of first-born infants, engaged couples, families of mental patients, and the like.

In general, then, material that is incisive, and does a good job of speaking to a smaller audience, is more likely to reach a larger audience than if aimed at too large a one from the beginning; and if the material is directed to a homogeneous audience, it is more likely to be effective than if the approach is discursive.

APPROPRIATENESS FOR THE AUDIENCE
FOR WHOM INTENDED

If there is something on your mind, some recent observation, or something you are annoyed about, you may be inclined to toss it into your writing without stopping to think whether or not it is relevant to your topic and appropriate for the audience you are addressing. For example, in an excellent piece for group workers written by a psychiatrist with a lot of experience, he tosses this comment into the foreword: "A more acceptable and effective psychiatry cannot evolve until more psychiatrists actively participate in community life and cease to be ivory tower spectators." You may agree with that idea completely, but is it relevant in a piece written for group workers? That is what a psychiatrist might appropriately say to other psychiatrists, but not to group workers.

Other examples of inappropriateness occur when the writer derogates an entire category of people—teachers, for instance, or psychologists, or parents, or community leaders. Still another type of inappropriateness is cynicism tossed in gratuitously; and another is bad jokes about the audience.

That brings us to the question of satire. Does satire have a place in mental health education? Many people say it does. I say that with an occasional rare exception it does not.

An example of a highly controversial bit of satire is the cartoon booklet *Pogo Primer for Parents* (15), written and illustrated by Walt Kelly for the Children's Bureau, a delightful booklet full of wit and charm, its devastating humor handled as only a master satirist can. I have never seen any-body yet who didn't get some good laughs out of it. Some educators say that is enough. I say it isn't. Here are some points for consideration on the matter of satire.

The genius of satire lies in the way it often illumines human foibles with profound insight. It *can* be free of rancor and hostility. But it rarely is! And that is my main point. Ordinarily, one does not have to analyze satire very carefully to recognize the undercurrent of cynicism and hostility. It masquerades as humor but it is almost never healthy, relaxed, carefree humor. People may laugh, but notice how often the laugh is self-conscious, apologetic, embarrassed. They are not laughing because they feel gay or relieved or entertained. They are laughing because a point has struck home and they wish to cover up their true feelings. As a device, satire more often than not tends to make people feel uncomfortable, ill-at-ease, self-conscious, less adequate, less whole, less accepting. Is *that* the goal of mental health education?

I realize that in declaring myself opposed to the use of satire I am in danger of being chalked up as being anti-humor and pro-ponderosity. Not true. I enjoy a bit of humor as much as the next person, even when it attacks my own sacred cows. The light touch is delightful, and often more effective than the heavy one. But satire, to be a good teaching technique, requires not only enormous skill but absolutely unambiguous motives, which it rarely has.

Notice that throughout the above discussion I have carefully hedged myself about with that word "rarely" and other qualifying phrases, and have indicated that there are exceptions. An example of the kind of satire that is first-rate is to be found in that entertaining little cartoon book *The Inside Story,* by Fritz Redlich and June Bingham (19). Most of the cartoons were taken from *The New Yorker* magazine, with commentary by the authors, pure satire, but non-hostile. The book has never had the distribution it deserves.

In summary: Be wary about using satire, for it is hardly ever what it seems. It can be useful, but rarely is it appropriate to the purposes of mental health education.

INTERNAL CONSISTENCY

WITH RESPECT TO THE AUDIENCE

Materials should not be addressed to mutually exclusive levels of understanding. If in the same publication you include both very simple and very complex or technical information, you may find that the part of your material that is simple enough for one audience is too simple for the other and vice versa. Thus you fall between two stools. You are either talking down to part of your audience or talking over the heads of the other part.

An example of this type of inconsistency is to be found in the report of the Cornell Conference on mental health education (3) where the editors suddenly interrupt what is supposed to be a report of a conference and toss in a twenty-page exegesis of psychiatric and psychoanalytic formulations and personality theory. The chances are that anybody who is motivated to read that report in the first place already knows more than twenty pages' worth about personality and psychoanalysis, but if he does not, then twenty pages is an entirely inadequate presentation of the subject. Many times in writing or planning a publication you gradually realize that you have either got to say more about your topic or omit it altogether. You are less likely to get carried away by your subject if you keep your audience constantly before your mind's eye.

THE QUALITY OF WRITING

Many people with professional training in fields such as psychiatry, psychology, and social work seem to be oblivious to qualitative differences in writing. Not only are they unable to distinguish between good and bad writing, but some of them do not even know there *is* a difference. After all, in the culture in which they move, everybody can write. So it does not occur to them to look upon writing as an activity requiring skill or effort, and they have never learned to appreciate good writing.

Yet how frequently communication failure can be traced to poor writing.

On the subject of "The Quality of Writing" the topics selected for comment here are style, clarity, tone, and organization.

STYLE

Many editors today are wailing over writers' deplorable obliviousness to style and the amount of execrable writing being turned out. The distinguished editor Alfred Knopf, in speaking of the inability of scholars to write well, says that he has given up hoping for style and that now all he longs for is "simple, straightforward, good English prose." He quotes the dean of a university law school as saying that at the law school, new students were so deficient in basic writing skills that the school was forced to operate as a "species of correctional institution." (Would that we had comparable correctional institutions in our medical schools, schools of social work, and some of the other centers for professional training in mental health.)

Style, like art, consists of imponderables, ineffables, and undefinables. That which makes style style is the same as that which makes art art. Since this is not a document on esthetics, or a writing course either, the only point relevant here is the reminder that there *is* such a thing as style. It should be subtle, not obvious. It may *be* self-conscious, but it should not *sound* self-conscious. Most people can improve their own style of writing by the simple device of paying attention.

CLARITY

Here we are back to the audience again. Will the *reader* consider the writing clear? I had an amusing experience recently. A psychiatrist had asked me to read a manuscript. It was one of those ponderous things bulging with four-syllable words and Latin endings five or six to the line. The contents were fine, but the writing awful. I thought that if the psychiatrist could hear a sample of his own writing he couldn't miss the point and my job would be done. So I picked out one of the worst of his sentences and read it aloud to him. I expected him to say "My gosh! Isn't that awful? Did I write that?" But what he did say was, musingly, "Funny. That's perfectly clear to me." Clear to *him*. It is not enough for something to be clear to the writer or to one's peers, especially if it is not intended for them. Unless it is clear to the *audience for whom intended,* it fails.

Is the reader sharply in focus? If you make a generalization, could the reader give an example? Could the reader paraphrase what you have just said? Could the reader sit down with a friend at dinner and tell him what your main points were? Incidentally, that is a useful gimmick for testing clarity. When you are trying to explain a complicated idea or interpret a complex program or project, do you think the reader would be able to describe to his friend what is going on, or what the needs are, or why a certain idea is significant? Sometimes just by examining the writing with this question in mind, you will see that the intended reader could not possibly be expected to understand it. So you try again.

Among the faults interfering with clarity are jargon, bad syntax, bad structure, ponderousness, unnecessary technicalities, and the like.

Jargon, meaning the technical or secret vocabulary of a science, along with a couple of its less polite synonyms, lingo and gibberish, is among the worst faults of professional writing. And once jargon is established in professional writing, it has a way of quickly finding its way into popular writing too.

As an example of jargon, here is how Blondie (11) was explained in the report of the Cornell Conference: "The purpose is to create an awareness of mental health as a comprehensive state of being involving a homeostatic relationship of emotions and body." How do you suppose Blondie would explain that to Dagwood?

This was an announcement in a professional journal: "Dr.

X has received a summer grant from X institution for a re-formulation of the theory underlying child guidance practice in situational terms avoiding dichotomization of concepts of unequal levels of abstraction."

And here is a description of a project for which financial support was being sought: "This is a means of communication for psychotherapeutic purposes depending on the creation of pictures which are elicited from the patient by the therapist to be used as guides to balance the verbal responses, because pictures as media provide freer expression of instinctual forces, and as arenae of action for self-integration wherein the patient working through the pattern-making need, establishes an equilibrium within himself."

This is the way one psychiatrist manipulated syntax: "Many an illness reflects the results, annoying to exasperating to terrifying, of an unsuccessful effort to cope with it."

Another example: "Although we need to make an exception for the anchorite, the saint, and the exceedingly rare isolate who is autonomously productive, it is unlikely that many individuals achieve a personal adjustment that is workable even at a primitive level, when the expressive component of their lives is absent or distinctly curtailed." This seems to say that people need a chance to express themselves creatively. Or does it?

Here are three quotations from three different speakers at a large luncheon for lay and professional people. All three were dealing with the same general topic. This was the opening sentence of one of the speakers: "Strangely enough the anomaly of our era is that the traditional American ideology which has always been antithetical to class conflicts actually exacerbates the tensions that develop between social groups in America."

This is what the second speaker had to say on the same topic: "When the adolescent is in rebellion for a new world and finds social scenes which reinstate and reinforce this rebellion, or when family pathology, a developmental stage of growth, an external deprivation, all come together, other situations develop in which pathology is nurtured."

Here is a third example still on the same subject, by a speaker with an entirely different manner of talking: "Belligerence always evokes belligerence. Friendliness always invites friendliness. Trust gradually builds trust. Children can be taught this about human nature every day of their lives on the basis of their actual experience with others." Which of those three is most likely to be comprehensible either to listener or reader?

TONE

It is curious how often a vaguely disagreeable note creeps into mental health writing. The substance, the content may be good but the tone is just plain unpleasant. Some writers seem unaware of how this will sound to the reader. An example of unpleasant tone is to be found in the opening summary paragraph on the first page of *Action for Mental Health* (8). Remember that this was a study requested *by* Congress and was written as a report *to* Congress, and therefore the target group was Congressmen. Here is the paragraph: "The philosophy that the Federal government needs to develop and crystallize is that science and education are resources—like natural resources—and that they deserve conservation through intelligent use and protection and adequate support—period. They can meet an ends test, but not a means test and not a timetable or appeal for a specified result. Science and education operate not for profit but profit everybody; hence they need adequate support from human society, whether this support comes from wise public philanthropy or private." How do you like that tone? Do you think the Congressman who reads that will think "How interesting!" Will he be eager to turn the page? How about the phrase, "they deserve . . . protection and adequate support—period"? Colloquialisms and slang have their place, but is this a good place?

Unpleasant tone also creeps into a lot of writing for parents, especially in the form of "blaming," or when the writer is obviously "taking sides"—parents versus children. It always seems strange that a therapist who would not dream of bopping his patient over the head during a therapeutic session seems to have not the slightest compunction about bopping him over the head with the written word.

Other points to be mentioned about tone are talking down to the audience and humor at the expense of the audience. If your humor is not light, then skip it. And the same thing goes for trying to be "cute," or any other striving for effect. If you have to reach for it, don't.

ORGANIZATION

Material can, of course, be over-organized: "My first point . . . My second point . . . My third point . . . ." When overdone this leads to heavy reading. But on the whole far more errors are committed by insufficient or careless organization than by over-organization. Books that are hastily thrown together usually betray that fact. Many books are excessively repetitious. Many would be twice as good if they were reduced by half, and would probably be read by twice as many people. The old gag "Tell 'em what you're going to tell 'em, then tell 'em, then tell 'em what you told 'em" may have been all right for 19th-century sermons, but for the 20th-century information explosion, brevity is to be recommended.

Speaking of the information explosion, there are certain adjustments we should all try to make to it. Striving for brevity is one of them. Many publications are longer than necessary. Watch people's reactions, the pleasure they express when they discover that a book they are obliged to read is small, or the moan that goes up when they see it is thick. Notice how one person will say to another "You ought to read it. It's not very big." Analyze figures on pamphlet distribution by comparison with book distribution. Notice what people reach for in display booths. All of these will indicate that brevity is highly regarded as a virtue.

The growing custom of putting a one-paragraph summary at the beginning of journal articles is to be applauded. Also there are many times when a summary is better at the beginning than at the end of a piece of writing. This technique in various forms is familiar to journalists but less so to people who have not been trained in writing.

Get into your subject quickly. How many readers do you suppose are lost by long meandering introductions? Then if on top of an introduction you add a preface and a foreword and a string of acknowledgments—good-bye reader. Always examine your "courtesy" sections to see which of them can be placed at the end instead of at the beginning.

MEDIUM AND FORMAT

Medium and format are special topics and actually do not belong in this chapter, but there are a few points it seems appropriate to mention here. The first one is the reminder that the written word and the spoken word are two different media—a point that seems to be forgotten all too often. When one is transposed verbatim to the other something is lost and there are few exceptions. Much regrettable waste of money and energy is to be found in verbatim reports of meetings and discussions. Some of this is sheer laziness. You have a meeting, you set up a tape recorder or hire a stenotypist if your budget permits, you get a transcription, somebody does a bit of touch-up editing, and off it goes to the printer. That is the easy way, and rarely worth the paper it is written on. *You cannot embalm the flavor of a discussion that way,* and you might as well not try.

Many innocent, not just lazy, mistakes are made as a result of trying to preserve in writing the give-and-take of face-to-face contacts. People go to a meeting, they find it valuable, they are excited about it, they want to preserve and share it. That is good. But you cannot preserve the spirit of a meeting by verbatim reproduction. There are ways you *can* do it but they take a lot more work. Next time you are deciding whether to spend a portion of your tight budget on fifty or seventy-five pages of "Proceedings" stop and think again.

Such documents turn up by the dozen in mental health literature, and are invariably dull.

With respect to format, a detail to be careful about is odd sizes and shapes. The layout people love to be "different," but as is the case with so many of the Madison Avenue techniques, they then begin to attribute value to difference for its own sake regardless of function. They particularly like large sizes. An office procedure to be recommended is that if something comes in that is so large or so queer a shape that it will not go into a standard file drawer and will not fit on a standard bookshelf, then it belongs in the round file—the wastebasket. Sometimes the excessively small things are a nuisance too.

Also be careful about things that are too gimmicky, or try too hard to be "arty" (in contradistinction to artistic). For instance, in a recent booklet the text was overlaid with charming pale green pictures, unusually pretty, a skillful job of silk screen printing. The only trouble was you couldn't read the text.

Leaflets with complex folds can be a nuisance, as bad as refolding a road map. Also, since in our culture we read from left to right, it seems a good idea to stick to that, even in publicity pieces. Another good idea is to have the front cover on the front and not on the back.

Now having argued against gimmicks and layout excesses, let me argue on the other side. Layout is exceedingly important. By and large not nearly enough attention is paid to it. It is desirable to enhance the attractiveness of a publication whenever you can. If you are planning large-scale distribution there are many times when a fee to a good layout person will be more than covered by increased sales. The readability of a typed or mimeographed report can be improved by attention to such simple details as margins, spacing, headings, underscoring, and capitalization.

Granted it is desirable to break up solid text for the sake of eye-appeal, nevertheless if the text is broken up solely for that purpose with complete disregard for meaning, it may interfere with readability. Headings and subheadings are desirable and on the whole are not used nearly enough, but they should be related to the context.

Publishers differ in their practice of where to locate the table of contents. Some love to bury it. In *Action for Mental Health*, for instance, it begins on page 35.

A strong argument can be made for placing it at the beginning where one can glance at it before starting to read and find it again if one wants to refer back to it later, especially if there is no index.

In summary, pay attention to format but don't go overboard, and don't let anybody push you overboard. Attractiveness is desirable but does not necessarily increase readability and may under some circumstances interfere with it. There is no virtue in being different merely for the sake of being different.

3

THE DEMAND FOR PROOF

CONCEPTS OF THE "HARD-NOSED SCHOOL"

"LINES OF EVIDENCE" IN EVALUATING MENTAL
HEALTH EDUCATION

   TRADITIONAL RESEARCH

   OBSERVATION OF AUDIENCE REACTION

   OPINION BASED ON EXPERIENCE

THE NATURE OF EVIDENCE

Criteria of Effectiveness
in Mental Health Education

"DOES IT WORK? HOW DO YOU KNOW? WHAT PROOF HAVE YOU?"

It was in 1948 that I wrote my first article on the subject of criteria of effectiveness in mental health education. That was after ten years of experience and thought and reading. During that period and for a number of years after that, I eagerly grabbed all the literature that had the word "evaluate" in it. I was intrigued, puzzled, bewildered, defensive. I am saying this here, not to try to impress the reader with how much I know, but with how involved and difficult I consider this subject to be; and how very, very important.

Educational material, the whole effort in mental health education: Does it work? How do you know? What proof have you? Then there is another question that must be added to round out these queries: "What do you do if you don't know?" It would be a nice little cliff-hanger if I could keep the reader in suspense until the end of this chapter, with the promise of a tidy list of definitive answers. But since I make no such promise, I shall give my reply first, lest I sound as if I thought I had any magic solution. What do you do if you don't know?

You do the best you can! That's as near as I can come to an answer, although I can elaborate it a little more than that and shall do so later.

THE DEMAND FOR PROOF

"How do you know?" "What proof have you?" These questions have great cogency. They are reasonable, proper, compelling questions in education, timely questions in the literal sense that they are in the spirit of the times. There is a lot of strength behind them; they cannot be ignored. People have a right to expect some answers, and if they do not get answers they have a right to feel bothered. Every serious mental health worker should be asking these questions of his own work and should be prepared to deal with them when other people ask them.

These questions have arisen partly as an outgrowth of modern science, because the demand for proof is a cornerstone of science. They have also arisen as a reaction to the long history of uncritical assumptions that have been made in mental health education, although uncritical assumptions are by no means unique to mental health education, for there are plenty of them throughout all education and all science too. There has been too little self-examination, too much taking it for granted that the student learns what the teacher thinks he is teaching, too much untested opinion, too much wishfulness. We have been lax in this field and we need to be pulled up. So let's keep on asking those questions. *But let's ask them in the right way.*

There are different ways of asking for proof. One way is to ask sincerely and searchingly and with complete intellectual honesty because you want to know the evidence and you don't want to be fooled. That is healthy skepticism in the true scientific spirit. But there are also other ways of asking for proof—for instance, to show that the other person doesn't know what he is talking about, which by definition makes you smarter than he is. You can also demand proof out of pessimism, or out of disappointment, or out of naïveté, or out of shock at discovering that there is less proof available than you had assumed. Questions stemming from these motivations have a way of turning into a kind of unhealthy skepticism. Instead of leading to a sincere search for evidence, they get twisted into the kinds of defeatism and destructiveness that block progress. And a great deal of that has been going on in mental health education in recent years.

One result of this kind of criticism is that it spreads the impression that disagreement in the field is greater than it is, that experts cannot agree on anything, that nobody knows anything about mental health education, and that it is impossible to prove that it has any effect whatever. This in turn leads to a loss of confidence all up and down the line. The public, including the people who hold the purse-strings, loses confidence in the educators, and the educators lose confidence in themselves. There are further results in that even the well-conceived programs of mental health education, those based on solid experience, fail to get integrated into total planning for mental health. We hear a great deal these days about "planning for planning" in mental health, but when you look at these plans, you find again and again that mental health *education* has been left out. Or among the groups with more experience, you can recognize it as being vaguely there but sort of bootlegged. In either case it is not there in the middle where it belongs, clearly spelled out and integrated with the over-all plan.

Now I challenge this excessive skepticism and downgrading. I feel it is regrettable and unnecessary and doing harm to the field. And I think that this attitude is one of the forces that has been interfering with progress in mental health education in recent years.

CONCEPTS OF THE "HARD-NOSED SCHOOL"

Another force interfering with progress in mental health education can be traced back to some of the faulty concepts of "the hard-nosed school." Or call them the logical positivists if you prefer. "Hard-nosed" is their word, not mine, and they love it. They're proud of it and equate it with being "truly scientific." They use the word "soft-nosed" with opprobrium. They think that in order to study any phenomenon "scientifically" you have to be able to count it, measure it, tabulate it, punch it on an IBM card, ink it on a tape, spot it on a curve, feed it into a computer, or tag it with a percentage or a correlation or a critical ratio or a P-value or something of the sort and if you can't do any of these things then it isn't science. Therefore you ignore it or deny the existence of it or disclaim any value or significance for it. This type of hard-nosed emphasis, however, is resulting in a whole new set of errors in the evaluation of mental health education.

At least four faulty concepts can be identified:

about how new knowledge is derived
about the nature of the subject matter
about the control of variables
about the nature of proof.

First, there is the concept that "research" is the *only* method by which new knowledge is derived. "Research" has become a fetish word these days, as if there were magic in it, so that "to do research" becomes an end in itself and conveys status. But there are many fallacies in this point of view. Research is not by any means the only way of obtaining new knowledge. Many outstanding thinkers have stated that idea forcefully. Alfred North Whitehead is one who is on record as deploring the assumption that the only way to find an answer or discover something new is through research. Abraham Maslow and Carl Rogers are two others who are highly articulate on the subject of "other ways of knowing."

There is also an assumption that just anybody can "do research," and that isn't true either. There are many people who are not qualified for it, and many who are using it as an escape from real-life confrontation with the problems they are researching. They are gratified when they come up with a bit of elegant methodology, but unfazed if their efforts produce only trivia. Many of these people are draining the pool of needed service personnel, while failing to produce results commensurate with the time, money, and staff allocated to their work. The amount of waste in research today is distressing to see and getting worse.

A second fault of the hard-nosed school is that they have failed to grasp the nature of the subject matter in mental health. Mental health education is concerned with such matters as feelings, attitudes, emotions, wishes, hopes, expectations, ambitions, values, motivation conscious and unconscious, goals, ideals, conflicts, drives, identification, compensation, love and hate, fear and anxiety, irrationality, coping mechanisms, the effects of life experiences, and so on. Those are the kinds of topics mental health education is and should be concerned with and those topics *will not be squeezed into the mold of the physical sciences*. They can rarely be measured or counted or statistically manipulated *in the same manner as* physical phenomena. That is not to say they cannot be studied scientifically. They can be. So please don't lift this point out of context. Please don't accuse me of being against science. It would be safer to be accused of being against mother-love. But I *am* saying that if you use the same models, the same techniques in trying to evaluate mental health education that you use with physical phenomena, you will not get significant answers. You will get wrong ones or at best trivia. Dr. Robert Oppenheimer, a scientist from the other side of the fence, from the hard-nosed side, makes the same point: "The worst of all possible misunderstandings," he says, "would be that psychology be influenced to model itself after a physics which is not there any more, which has been quite outmoded."

A third weakness of the hard-nosed school has been their inability to grasp the implications of the cataract of variables, which is more a problem in this field than in the physical sciences.

One way of trying to cope with variables is through a "research design" (another term that has come into vogue only in recent years) which usually calls for a control group to be compared with an experimental group. But when you examine those control groups, you often find they are not truly control groups; they merely differ from the experimental group with respect to some one or several variables that have been arbitrarily selected. What's more, you may find that the most significant factors of all have been "controlled out" because they were too difficult to manage. Therefore one should not be overly impressed by the claim of "a control group" unless it manages to control the significant variables.

The final error lies in failing to grasp the nature of proof. The hard-nosed people are repeatedly trapped in the fallacy of the equation that unproven is identical with untrue. They would deny it. But then they proceed *as if* it were so—that is, as if unproven means untrue. That occurred, for instance, in the Cornell Conference report. The authors say: "That this knowledge is unproven does not make it untrue—failing to prove something is different from disproving it." An excellent statement. It could not be said better. But despite giving lip-service to this idea, the report is shot through with the opposite idea, namely, that if you cannot positively "prove" that mental health education *is* effective, then it is *not* effective.

I have dwelt at length on the concepts I think are interfering with the proper development of mental health education, and I have pinned a good deal of blame on the hard-nosed school. That is because, as mentioned above, I feel that these emphases have been at least partly responsible for the downgrading of mental health education in the last few years, which has resulted in weakening many mental health education programs and, in a few documented instances, destroying them altogether. I think it is high time the behavioral sciences put the logical-positivistic emphasis in its place. The pendulum has swung too far in the direction of glorification of methodology, of mechanistic-behavioristic techniques, of "research" as the sole way of arriving at new knowledge, and of a demand for a type of "proof" that does not exist. That does not mean I am any less respectful of the truly scientific than are the logical positivists. We are indebted to them for some salutary "pointing out." We must not toss out any of the methodological gains they have brought us. We should *build on* their techniques and *integrate* them with other approaches. But we should not rely on their techniques too heavily, or permit a new set of mistakes to arise and replace the old ones they are inveighing against.

This would be the place to push back still further and examine such phrases as "concepts of knowing," "objective," "subjective," and the like. There are many new and exciting ideas now developing around these terms, but it would take us too far afield to discuss them here. Suffice it to say that it is becoming more and more apparent that we need a reformulation of concepts of knowing and we are beginning to get it from the new humanistic psychology. This will come up again in the last chapter.

"LINES OF EVIDENCE" IN EVALUATING MENTAL HEALTH EDUCATION

Now back to the question "What proof have you?" I have reached the point in my own thinking where I would like to drop the words "prove" and "proof" from my vocabulary and use entirely different words. Instead of talking about proof, for the time being I would prefer to talk about "lines of evidence," that is, lines of evidence in evaluating mental health education. So I have listed some of the lines of evidence I think can be helpful in evaluation, instead of striving for absolute out-and-out "proof." They fall into three categories: traditional research; observation of audience reaction; and opinion based on experience.

TRADITIONAL RESEARCH

Although I have been excoriating traditional research when improperly conceived, it *of course* belongs right in the middle of the picture when properly conceived. We *must* have *formal controlled experimentation.* We cannot get along without it.

We need just exactly the kind of rigid research that has been criticized here. But more of it should be good and less of it mediocre or trivial. The calibre of research should be improved. It should be selective in all ways: more selective with respect to the people who are doing it; more selective in the kind of thing that is done; more selective in the papers that are presented at professional meetings and in professional journals; tighter strings on the budgets devoted to research; higher standards of professional acceptability. But nevertheless, it would be formal, controlled experimentation.

A second type of traditional research would be studies of historical evidence, particularly studies of the cumulative effects of mental health education. Examples are studies of changing attitudes toward specific problems of children, such as eating habits or two-year-old negativism; changes in child-rearing practices such as permissiveness; changes in the handling of crises such as separation of mother and child and hospitalization of child; changes in public attitudes toward mental illness.

OBSERVATION OF AUDIENCE REACTION

Call this target-group reaction, if you wish, including readers of course. Or call it "feedback" if you prefer. This means reports by the audience, which are practically always in the form of value judgments.

We are now seeing some changes in the weight we are willing to accord to value judgments. We went through a period when a mere "expression of opinion" was scorned. It wasn't scientific. If you went to a meeting and came away saying that it was stimulating, a wonderful meeting, you got a lot out of it—that meant nothing to a researcher, because it was "just an opinion." But this is gradually changing, and we are beginning to be less fearful of subjective reactions and value judgments. We are seeing that some of the elegant research designs are worthless exactly because they fail to take into consideration just that kind of thing.

Here is a letter Dr. Loyd Rowland received a number of

years ago from a mother who had been receiving the *Pierre the Pelican* (21) series of letters for parents of first-born children:

> I am more than happy to write you thanking you for your information. They seems as if I was talking together over problems which I was trying to solve. While thinking about problems it seems as if someone knock and said, "May I come in? My name is Pierre. I am from the Department of Health. I can help you with your baby. I know many things about babies." As I read I would find myself about to say "Thanks," but it was only a message through the mail. Yes, it was only a message through the mail and I has enjoyed your message.

Would you say that that mother got anything from the Pierre letters? Would you be willing to brush away such a response because you could not handle it statistically? Dr. Rowland has hundreds of letters like that from Pierre readers. Stack those up against questionnaires designed to be fed into a computer. Suppose they disagree. Which is more meaningful? The point is that when there is that kind of feedback from the audience it is significant, even if it cannot be squeezed into a research design.

Another important form of audience reaction is the demand for material. I maintain that when a piece of material is exceptionally well received by the audience for whom it is intended, that fact is of some significance in trying to evaluate it. I have been criticized for this point of view by my associates who insist that the fact that a piece is well liked by the audience is no evidence of value whatever. They have a point. But I argue that if you produce a piece of material—a film, a pamphlet, a book, a TV show, a dramatic sketch—and if it proves to be enormously popular so that there is continued and repeated demand, for instance a pamphlet that is published and republished in the hundreds of thousands and constantly cited in bibliographies, or a book that has to be reprinted time after time, or a dramatic sketch or film that people keep on asking for year after year: if you find that kind of popularity, then that is significant. Notice that I do not for an instant use the word "proof"; I am not saying that popularity is proof of value. But I do say that that kind of popularity is one of the lines of evidence indicating that there is something of value there that you should take a look at. The audience might be entirely wrong, and I agree with all my critics in this respect. It could be a lousy piece of material. It could be completely and totally unsound. But it rarely is. In fact I doubt whether it ever is. I have more confidence in people than that. It is a little like self-selection of food by infants. Babies, when free to select, do not continue to choose food that is bad for them. Animals do not continue to eat herbs that poison them. My observation is that bad material does not get perpetuated to any considerable extent. The bad stuff is more likely to fade away and be forgotten. The good stuff lasts. There are exceptions, but this seems to be the general rule.

It should be clear, however, that this applies only in circumstances in which the demand is natural and spontaneous, and "from the people." The big distribution that comes about as the result of skillful and aggressive promotion is something else again. For instance, in one situation a pamphlet was prepared as part of a national promotion and fund-raising campaign, offered free, and advertised with all the skills of a national advertising agency behind it. People were urged to send for free copies and did so. The large distribution figures that resulted were not evidence of popularity at all, but rather that the title was appealing and that people love anything free.

An example of demand "from the people" that continues decade after decade is the Children's Bureau's pamphlet *Infant Care* (12), of which some fifty million copies have been distributed since it was first published in 1914. Another long-lived item is *Some Special Problems of Children: Aged Two to Five Years,* by Nina Ridenour and Isabel Johnson, which has topped the million mark in distribution in this country and has been translated into several foreign languages including Japanese (20). Another is the leaflet *Mental Health Is . . . 1, 2,3,* which has been reprinted in scores of other publications—

magazines, newspapers, industrial bulletins, brochures of mental health associations—in addition to having been endlessly quoted in part (17). It was not intended to make mental health "sound easy," but rather to explain "what we are talking about." Some of the publications of the Child Study Association of America have been in demand for twenty or thirty years, and so have a number of the pamphlets of Science Research Associates and the Public Affairs Committee. And some of the dramatic sketches of *Plays for Living,* formerly American Theatre Wing Community Plays (18), are such perennial favorites that they are produced year after year after year. I am convinced that that kind of popularity is motivated by recognition of validity on the part of the audience for whom intended, and that it is a line of evidence worthy of attention in evaluating the material.

In addition to demand from the audience there are other minor types of audience behavior that deserve passing mention. Did you ever hear of the Wiggle Test? That was a creation of the motion picture industry many years ago, and is probably familiar to every schoolteacher in the world. The film promoters used to apply it very seriously when they were pretesting films for children. While the film was being shown to an audience of children, adult observers would stand against the walls and watch, not the film, but the children, to see how much wiggling went on. The less wiggling, the more money they were willing to invest.

In the early days of the American Theatre Wing Community Plays, on the night of the premiere we used to watch carefully for what we called the "Kaffee Klatsch." These were little knots of people who would gather over cokes in the corner drug store after the play and could be overheard discussing it. We did not have to sit up all night waiting for the reviews in the morning paper, since no reviewer and no paper knew we existed. But if we saw a few Kaffee Klatsches congregating then we knew we had a hit, and went home happy.

This type of observation also applies to PTA meetings and discussion groups of all kinds. If the people hang around so long the janitor has to come and turn the lights out, that is *usually* the sign of a good meeting.

Another way of observing reaction is to try to find out whether the intended reader, of a pamphlet for instance, has voluntarily and spontaneously passed it on to someone else. We once tried that out with some pamphlets in the Child Health Stations of the New York City Department of Health. We were trying to figure out simple devices for finding out whether the pamphlets were used. We did not seem to get very far with asking the mothers obvious questions such as "Did you read it?" and "What did you think?" because many of them were not articulate enough to give a meaningful reply. When we asked "Did your husband read it?" and "Did you pass it on to anyone else?" we seemed to get more significant results. If the mother passed it on to somebody else, that seemed to be a sign that the piece was more effective than if she had not.

OPINION BASED ON EXPERIENCE

As mentioned above, the word "opinion" is often swept away scornfully as if it had no value. True, it is frequently valueless, frequently undependable, frequently just plain wrong. *But research does not necessarily give any better answers.* It is possible to develop all sorts of skills—teaching, for instance, or therapy, or leading discussions, or group work— skills based on experience, without waiting for "more research." With enough solid experience one should be able to say, "This approach works better than that one," or "This method is better than that." There is a richness in the firsthand experience of the people doing the job that we are foolish to ignore.

Related to opinion as a line of evidence is the *integration of research data with practitioners' experience.* This is the point at which research and experience reinforce each other. Conventional research so often proves to be trivial or irrelevant unless it is related to experience. Conversely, experience needs to be checked by research whenever feasible. An interesting example of purposeful effort at integrating the two is to be found in the book *Review of Child Development Research* (6). The authors have tried in every instance to correlate and supplement research findings with the opinions and experience of practitioners in the field, with the result that the material they present is far richer than either "research" or "opinion" would be alone.

Not to be overlooked in evaluation of effectiveness is *accretion of evidence*. The first time I came across the term "faggot theory" was in the work of the British psychiatrist John Bowlby. Whether he was the first to use the term I do not know, but it expresses an idea that has particular cogency for mental health education, even though it is sometimes criticized. Bowlby's point—and incidentally some of the authors of articles in the *Review of Child Development Research* express the same idea—is that it is very difficult to get complete and definitive evidence of any kind. But if you have data that produce one little line of evidence pointing in this direction and another little line pointing in the same direction and then another and another and another all pointing in the same direction, then you put them together like a bundle of faggots. Perhaps each twig alone is not very strong, but when bound together they become something quite sturdy. The hard-nosed people scoff at this. Nevertheless, you could line up a long list of examples in the mental health field where no single piece of evidence is definitive but when put together they are impressively conclusive.

Here is what Bowlby had to say a number of years ago in the monograph *Maternal Care and Mental Health* in which he reported some of his first studies on maternal separation (1). (Those studies, by the way, have elicited a wide gamut of reactions—first being taken as gospel, then torn to pieces as "unscientific," now coming back into respect—which is what happens to a lot of good work.) He was reporting on the research and experience of a great many people on the subject of parent-child separation, and he said: "The extent to which these studies undertaken by people of many nations, varied training, and as often as not ignorant of each other's conclusions confirm and support each other is impressive. What each individual piece of work lacks in thoroughness, scientific reliability or precision is largely made good by the concordance of the whole. Nothing in scientific method carries more weight than this."

A final line of evidence relevant here is the *cumulative, shared wisdom of sensitive, knowledgeable, and experienced professional workers.* That is quite a string of words but each one is in there for a reason.

Cumulative refers to the gradual accumulation of experience that gives perspective. When this is disregarded, the work will suffer. If you plunge into a situation or a piece of work without any knowledge of what has gone before, you are likely to commit the same mistakes as your predecessors, plus a few more of your own. A great deal of this is happening in mental health these days. Not enough attention is paid to the past, either to the mistakes of the past or to the successes of the past. How can anyone learn from the past if he does not know what the past is? That is why in these chapters I have put much emphasis on *mistakes,* in the hope that we can learn from them.

Shared: cumulative, *shared* experience. This is where some of the multidiscipline efforts come in. But it is not a simple matter of just throwing together a bunch of people from different disciplines. Often what emerges from that situation is little more than friction and chaos. There has to be something more in the plan or in the leadership, something that will bring about some kind of amalgamation or fusing or integration of points of view, each enriching the other, so that what finally comes out is a new whole, something that is more than the sum of its parts.

Wisdom. Wisdom is a terribly old-fashioned word but I boldly propose that we reinstate it. The Old Testament sages seemed to think it expressed a valuable idea then. Perhaps we would do well to pay more attention to it now.

Sensitive. There are people in all fields who are callous and impersonal and insensitive, and that includes many people in mental health. But there are many who are exceedingly sensitive, too, and that is where the role of intuition comes in, the "clinical hunch," the "born" teacher, the "natural" leader. People trying to do mental health education need to have a certain kind of sensitivity. If they do not have it, if they are oblivious to the feelings of others, if they antagonize their audience, they are less likely to be effective as educators.

Knowledgeable. Here comes another old-fashioned word: "moral"—the moral obligation to be informed, to know what you are talking about. It is always regrettable when people carrying responsibility feel no sense of obligation for acquiring a solid body of knowledge about the field in which they are operating.

Experienced. There is no substitute for experience. You cannot be experienced to start with but you certainly can start to accumulate experience, although that too is not foolproof. Someone may have had twenty years of experience but it may have been twenty years of experience in repeating the same mistakes. So it is true that although experience alone is not a complete safeguard, nevertheless it is usually something pretty valuable. There seems to be a kind of vogue nowadays that implies not only that you do not need to know anything about a field to work in it, but that you cannot be "objective" if you do know anything about it. And there have been some shocking instances of that. A recent one was where a person was chosen to do a major study of mental health education *because* he had no background of any kind in mental health education or any related subject that would qualify him for research, on the theory that therefore he would be "objective." Of course there is often excellent reason for bringing in new blood, somebody from the outside to take a look at what insiders can no longer see, somebody with special or different skills, the multidiscipline approach. That is good. What is to be deplored is the situation in which somebody without background in a field is brought in to make judgments when the complexities and implications of the data are more than anybody could be expected to grasp in a short time. This modern attitude that it is not necessary to know anything about the subject in order to deal with it, this new premium on ignorance, accounts for more than a little of the research trivia and the mediocrity and ineffectiveness of many mental health programs.

To repeat: one of the "lines of evidence" as to the effectiveness of mental health education will be found in the *cumulative, shared wisdom of sensitive, knowledgeable and experienced professional workers*. Each of those words contains an idea that should not be overlooked in evaluating programs.

THE NATURE OF EVIDENCE

Now, to go back to the final question, the one with which this chapter opened: "What do you do if you don't know whether your material is effective?" Do you give up and quit? Do you say, "We won't undertake any education because we can't prove it is effective?" Or, do you go ahead and do the best you can? Here are two quotations on this point, both of them having to do with child care, but both also applicable across the board in mental health education. One of them comes again from Bowlby, from the same monograph quoted earlier. He says:

> True, the evidence presented in this report is at many points faulty. Many gaps remain unfilled. The critical information is often missing, but it must be remembered that evidence is never complete, that knowledge of truth is always partial, and that to await certainty is to await eternity.

The other quotation comes from Leon Yarrow in the *Review of Child Development Research*:

> In this area we have few unequivocally established facts, but child care practices and programs cannot wait on definitive findings. We can only proceed on the basis of what seems to be the most adequate knowledge at the present time and avoid extremes in practice that violate common sense or good clinical intuition.

4

PLANNING THE PROGRAM

  GOALS

  DEFINITIONS

  LIMITS

  CRITERIA FOR DECISIONS

  EDUCATION "FOR" AND "ABOUT" MENTAL HEALTH

  LEVELS OF PREVENTION

  TARGET GROUPS

PLANNING THE MATERIALS

  SELECTION

  USE

  BUILDING PROGRAM FROM MATERIALS

  DEVELOPMENT OF NEW MATERIALS

Materials in Relation to Program

"HOW YOU PLAN"

The subject of the seminars out of which these chapters grew was "Materials" and not "Program," but naturally one cannot get very far in talking about materials except against a background of program. Therefore it seems appropriate to devote some space to the principles of program planning in mental health education, with emphasis on what might be called the symbiotic relationship between program and materials.

PLANNING THE PROGRAM

In program planning there are many choices. It is unfortunate when a program merely grows like Topsy. And many programs do grow just that way. Any program is likely to be stronger if it is planned with full awareness of alternatives. Many points need to be considered.

GOALS

Often in program planning one of the first topics to come up is goals: "What are our (your, their) goals?" With respect to goals it is important to differentiate between far goals and near goals. For the far goals, let your imagination soar. Let your dreams, your hopes, your ideals become your goals. Do not be afraid of all the fine beautiful phrases such as "welfare of mankind," the "worth and dignity of the individual," health as "a state of complete physical, mental and social well-being." You do not even have to be afraid of such words as "happiness,"—"adjustment,"—"peace,"—"all the people." And if you want to talk in the language of humanistic psychology you can talk about "self-actualization," "self-realization," "the human potentiality," and the like.

Unquestionably, ideals are basic to the mental health effort. We do not have enough of them. *But they have to be implemented.* Ideals are the motivation, the push, the driving force, but you can't build a program around ideals. And some of the worst program failures occur because people think they can.

So against the background of hopes and wishes and ideals and other far goals, you have to be clear about your near goals. You have to come down to earth. You have to decide what you're going to *do.* The action takes place right down here, not up in the stratosphere of wishfulness. In order to avoid friction and wasted energy among people who may have the same ideals but little else in common, you have to arrive at agreement about how to proceed.

The dilemma of differences in opinion about goals was illustrated in the Cornell Conference report. In the chapter on "Goals," one person thought the goal of mental health education should be education in psychodynamics and mental mechanisms. Another said it should be educating the public to recognize psychiatric emergencies. A third said it should be to achieve the desegregation of the mentally ill. And a fourth said it should be the dissemination of knowledge about existing resources.

When these four statements are examined from the point of view of how one would build a program around them, it becomes apparent that four completely different programs would emerge from those four goals. The programs would have no resemblance to each other whatever. The dilemma here is a familiar one: the problem posed when people assume they are like-minded but discover they are different-minded.

DEFINITIONS

In the course of planning you will inevitably be challenged, or you may challenge yourself, to "define your terms." And here is where similar complications arise. You sit down with your group, presumably to talk about the same thing, but it quickly emerges that different members are thinking along different lines.

Trying to define mental health and mental health education can be a salutary experience if you have never tried it. Try it all by yourself. Then try it in a group. Try it in a group of like-minded people, then in a group of unlike-minded people. You may be in for some surprises.

The examples above illustrate how widely people may differ with respect to what a term such as mental health education means to them. But some of the other related words we use vary just as widely. Recently I got a shock when a speaker, an authority on communication, gave as his definition of communication "to get somebody to do what you want them to do." Maybe that's O.K. for soap and cigarettes but it will quickly wreck a mental health program. Even the word education is subject to wide deviations. For instance, among some organizations, "public education" means "to educate people to give money." This may sound innocuous but if that definition is accepted, what happens next is that fund-raising becomes the goal of the organization and program becomes subsidiary to fund-raising. Somebody else says education means "to change people in the direction you want them to go." "*You?*" So these are just a few examples to show how widely people may differ when they think they are talking about the same thing.

LIMITS

Nothing in program planning is more important than *setting realistic limits*. When an organization sets unrealistic limits, it is often because people have not brought their goals down to earth. Unrealistic limits may emerge from the highest and best motives. People are so eager to correct defects and accomplish big things that they are not sensitive to the limits to what can be accomplished under the circumstances. Therefore along with saying what you *are* going to do, it may be a good idea to say what you are *not* going to do in order not to let your work become too scattered. This point is likely to be illustrated when almost any group of mental health staff people get together and start sharing their experiences with the problems that arise when they are under pressure to spread themselves too thin or to undertake inappropriate activities.

What is it reasonable to expect you *can* accomplish? Not pie-in-the-sky. Not desk-dreaming. But what *can* you do about whatever it is you are *trying* to do? The dilemma of discursiveness is a very great problem in mental health. Sometimes it seems as if it were more than coincidence that the word "discursive" includes the word "curse," because discursiveness is truly a curse of the mental health field.

Discursiveness arises partly because of the ambiguity of the term "mental health" and partly because of the scope of the field. When somebody is trying to get you to enlarge your program or stretch your budget to cover another project, or take on activities for which there is not enough staff, often they will say, "But *that* is mental health too" or "That has *implications* for mental health." And almost surely they will be right. It is hard to name anything that does not have *implications* for mental health—housing, recreation, civil rights, foreign policy, local politics, art, religion, the population explosion—everything you mention has implications for mental health. But it does not follow that an agency trying to do a mental health job can become involved in everything that somebody says has "implications for mental health." You will soon be in over your heads. You therefore need to be firm in limiting your program to that part of the mental health job that is your charge and in which you think you can accomplish something.

How do you make up your mind? What criteria do you use in making decisions about program? Of course, sometimes the staff has few choices because the program has already been sharply defined. But often the staff has a lot of choice and at times more choice than it is aware of. In making a decision it is important to differentiate between *need* and *competence.* Even though it may be agreed that something *needs* to be done, it does not necessarily follow that the organization has the *competence* to do it. The need is invariably there. For "human need is without boundary." It is not hard to justify need. But what can your organization *do* about it? Therefore, the question should be re-phrased: not "Is there a need?", but "Can we do something about it?" Do you already have the competence or can you develop it or mobilize it?

One of the factors entering into the decision about whether a given need is or is not part of your responsibility centers around the question of whether there are already other agencies charged with responsibility for that area. There are innumerable areas that overlap mental health or that contain a large mental health component—delinquency, day care, pastoral training, teacher training, child health, student health; one could name fifty like that. The question becomes sticky when there are other agencies charged with responsibility for that area, but you think they are neglecting the mental health aspects of their job. So what do you do? Do you jump in and add that field to the rest of your responsibilities, because there is a *need* and because you are dissatisfied with the other agencies? In the past, mental health groups have not been noted for their humility. Too often they have plunged in as "experts" and then discovered (or failed to discover) that the other group had a vast background that made some of the mental health recommendations seem amateurish indeed. Therefore before you move into a new field it is wise to stop and think, "Can *we* do any better?" Sometimes you will decide you probably cannot. Also stop to think whether you have fully explored the question of working *with* the other organizations. Many splendid examples of interagency cooperation are to be found in mental health, many groups that have worked out excellent collaborative relationships. It may take some extra work and headaches, but it often pays off in the long run.

EDUCATION "FOR" AND "ABOUT"

MENTAL HEALTH

In defining type of program operation there are two phrases that delineate in a broad, loose sort of way the chief subject matter or direction of the program. One is "education about mental illness and mental health"; the other is "education for mental health." The phrases themselves are nothing more than a gimmick to try to differentiate two types of program emphases.

Actually, the two types of program thus described are very different from each other. "Education *about* mental illness and mental health" is to inform people of the facts so they will be better prepared to fulfill their responsibilities as citizens. It applies more to mental illness and mentally ill people than it does to mental health. It covers many of the public information and public relations functions, publicity, and interpretation of institutions, services, community organization, and community needs. The purpose is to get people to support activities on behalf of the mentally ill whether the support be in the form of contributions, approval of increased government expenditures, legislation, personal participation in the voluntary effort, or whatever it may be.

"Education *for* mental health" applies more to the mental health approach than to the concern for mental illness as such. "Education *for*" is used in the sense of giving people the kind of background and understanding that will enable them to make a better adjustment in their own lives and in their relations with others and to be more helpful to the people for whom they are responsible. This covers a wide range of subject matter: psychodynamics, self-understanding, child development, parent education, family life education, to name a few.

LEVELS OF PREVENTION

Another important decision in program planning has to do with the level of prevention with which the program is primarily concerned. One level of prevention is not necessarily *better than* another. There is a job to be done at each level. There seems to be a lot of misunderstanding on this, chiefly because people have not thought things through. For instance, there is often the assumption, usually unstated, that prevention is somehow superior to care. Yet somebody has to do the care job; somebody has to look after the mentally ill and do it properly. And we certainly know that even right now, in the 1960's, care of the mentally ill is still in many places so grossly neglected as to continue to be a national disgrace.

So the point is not that prevention is *superior*; it is *different*. True, it makes better sense to try to prevent an illness than merely to keep on caring for it, and that is usually the reasoning of groups that are in the process of planning new programs or shifting program emphasis. At first perhaps they are concerned about hospitals. But soon they begin to ask questions about prevention, and that is good. That is the direction in which their thinking should move. It is constructive for them to be pondering how these terrible diseases can be prevented. But what happens in real life is that they may become preoccupied with *trying* to prevent, without any assurance that the measures they are advocating actually *do* prevent, and meanwhile the other side of the job—the care, the treatment—gets neglected. That is why it is necessary to keep stressing that one is not better than the other. Both jobs must be done, and it is often a matter of choice which program an agency chooses to emphasize.

We are indebted to public health for helping delineate certain concepts relevant to mental health. For years it has been apparent that mental health had much to learn from public health; and it has been disappointing that mental health seemed to learn so slowly. But now at last some of the principles and concepts of public health seem to be creeping into mental health.

When standard public health terms—primary, secondary, tertiary prevention—are applied to mental health, tertiary prevention refers to reducing the impairment resulting from mental disorder; secondary prevention reduces the duration of mental illness; and primary prevention reduces the incidence of mental disorder in a community.

By those definitions, an example of tertiary prevention would be helping a recovered mental patient regain his place in the community. Rehabilitation would be under that heading. Rehabilitation is prevention only in the sense that it keeps a mentally ill person from being useless and becoming a burden. It is preventive in that it prevents helplessness or dependence on the community.

Secondary prevention would be the care and treatment, inpatient or outpatient, of a person already identified as being mentally ill or emotionally disturbed, whether a child or an adult. That is prevention in the sense that it tries to keep the patient from staying sick or getting worse and tries to help him recover.

Primary prevention means to do what needs to be done to keep emotional disturbance from occurring in the first place. That is more literally prevention than either of the other two. All three of them *can* be called prevention but it is more usual to use the word prevention to mean primary prevention.

That the concept of prevention has been changing becomes apparent if one thinks back over the history of mental health in this country during the past five or six decades. Think, for instance, of the early child guidance clinics from which so much of the whole mental health effort has stemmed. The first child guidance clinic, Dr. William Healy's first clinic in 1912, was established "to prevent delinquency," which was also the purpose stated for the first of the demonstration clinics set up by the Commonwealth Fund in the early 1920's. That can, of course, be called preventive psychiatry, but actually it is only halfway back in prevention, because it is trying to prevent something from getting worse after it has already been recognized as a problem.

One can think about prevention in terms of levels, but it can also be thought of as a "pushing-back process." That changes the concept from levels to ongoing process, which is more dynamic. A public health analogue dating back to the 15th or 16th century is found in the custom of giving onions and lemons to sailors to cure scurvy *after* the sailors had already developed scurvy. Then they began to realize the importance of fresh foods on long ocean trips, and made more of an effort to get them in order to *prevent* scurvy in the first place. That was the pushing-back process: preventing something bad, preventing a specific illness. Then gradually came the stress on good diet for good health which is true primary prevention. These days in our child health conferences, we do not talk to mothers about good nutrition in order to prevent any specific disease, but good nutrition for good health.

The same principle holds in mental health. Just as in physical health, in mental health we now know enough to prevent some of the specific disorders, for instance some of the neuroses (though not some of the worst of the mental disorders such as schizophrenia). And we do know a lot about improving mental health in general. Thus the whole preventive effort becomes one continuous "pushing-back process."

TARGET GROUPS

In listing the various target groups involved in mental health education, both those at the educator end and those on the receiving end, it is hard to come up with satisfactory words. (Two that are frequently used are "gatekeepers" and "caretakers," but I have always disliked both of those because I feel they have unfortunate connotations.) One way to divide the groups is to call those responsible for mental health education in any of its aspects "purveyors" and those on the receiving end "consumers." The list then shapes up like this:

Purveyors
    Core professional groups
    Related professions (or related helping professions)
    Interpreters
Consumers
    Intermediate consumers
    Ultimate consumers

Core professional groups traditionally include psychiatrists, clinical psychologists, psychiatric social workers, and psychiatric nurses: people whose professional training is geared specifically toward qualifying them to work in the field of mental health and particularly to work with mentally and emotionally disturbed individuals.

Related groups or the related helping professions are the people who are working in a helping or serving capacity. These are the people whose primary job is not dealing with mental or emotional disorders *as such*, but people who in the course of their work are in a strategic position to do so and therefore to do preventive mental health work if they themselves have some grounding in mental health. A short basic list, with emphasis on certain sub-categories, might include: physicians, with emphasis on general practitioners, pediatricians, and obstetricians; nurses, and among nurses especially public health nurses; teachers, particularly nursery school teachers; the clergy; and law-enforcement officials, especially the police, who are often called "our first-line psychiatrists."

Interpreters would include the people who deal with the production and distribution of material prepared primarily for the purpose of explaining or interpreting a piece of work or promoting an organization: public information officers and public relations people in mental health organizations; writers, authors, and journalists specializing in mental health. These people may or may not have had previous professional training in one of the core or related professions.

Intermediate consumers refers to the people to whom mental health material is directed for use in their professional capacity. For instance, if material is written for a nurse to use with mothers or certain specified types of patients, then the nurse is in the category of intermediate consumer, because the intent is that she will pass on the information or ideas to others. Professionals are to be thought of as intermediate consumers if the effectiveness of the material is to be measured by the extent to which the ideas get passed on down the line. Material prepared for them is usually, though not necessarily, at a higher level than the material prepared for the ultimate consumer; and it is most effective if it can be incorporated into their basic training and education or their in-service training, or preferably in both.

Ultimate consumers means the people you are trying to reach in the end: parents, or special categories of parents such as parents of young children, parents of adolescents, parents of handicapped children; or families, such as families of the mentally ill; employers, such as employers of the mentally ill; or disadvantaged young people; or adolescents, young marrieds, the aged, clinic patients, or any other category.

The category approach will save a lot of fumbling in developing sound program. If the various purveyors and intermediaries are kept clearly in mind, it is easier to mark out the channels for reaching the ultimate consumer.

Now that I have used the word "reaching," let me pause for a moment to discuss it. That is one of the words that fool us. We speak glibly of "reaching people"—"We reached x number of people"—all of us talk that way at times—when actually what we mean is to say that x number of people *may* have been exposed to a given piece of material. If you hand out 10,000 leaflets at a county fair, is that "reaching" 10,000 people? If you put up a poster where 10,000 people pass daily, have you "reached" 10,000 people? If you put on a film or a dramatic sketch or pass out free pamphlets at a clinic or hospital or child health conference, are you "reaching" everybody exposed to the material?

Obviously in any given situation it is impossible to know

what proportion of the people who are "exposed to" something are also "reached by" it. That does not mean we should drop the word "reach." It is a useful word. If we dropped every word that proves ambiguous we would soon have no vocabulary. It only means that when we use the word we should do so with at least a small reservation in the backs of our minds that whispers "Maybe we're reaching them and maybe we're not."

The question of "reaching" comes under special scrutiny when we talk about what is nowadays frequently described as the "hard-to-reach groups." Ordinarily that refers to various disadvantaged groups—the culturally deprived, low socioeconomic levels, people with limited education. Recently it has been tied in with the Antipoverty Program and some of its sub-divisions such as Head Start and the various opportunities-for-youth efforts. It is a good idea to remember, however, that "hard-to-reach" is by no means limited to those groups. (And it has even been said that of all hard-to-reach groups the hardest to reach are doctors.) Let us agree for the moment, though, that "hard-to-reach" refers primarily to disadvantaged groups.

It is constantly being said that mental health education programs must make more of an effort "to reach the hard-to-reach." *That is a concept I wish to challenge.* I maintain that "hard-to-reach" is not a good basis for a program of mental health education particularly if you are trying to reach the people directly. The concept "hard-to-reach" is inconsistent with such ideas as readiness and motivation, which should form the cornerstone of mental health education programs. Needless to say, there should be all kinds of efforts directed toward reaching the hard-to-reach, but what I am challenging is whether it is a good idea to try to reach them through traditional mental health education techniques, especially the written word.

Among disadvantaged groups, there is usually a problem of limited education, which means that the people are usually non-readers in the sense that they do not rely on reading for pleasure or leisure and are not accustomed to or fully at ease with the written word. For them the written word is not a natural medium. Therefore it seems obvious that they would be less "reachable" through the written word than are people who are more accustomed to reading.

There is a naïve notion around that if you want to reach people with limited education, you simplify your material— you use short words and sentences, fewer Latin endings, more imperatives, more pictures. But just how far down the line can one go in simplifying mental health *ideas* and still have them meaningful? You cannot continue to dilute and dilute because if you do, presently all the depth and significance goes out of what you are trying to say. Therefore you have to use methods other than the written word in trying to reach disadvantaged groups with limited education. (The extent to which pictures —comic books and cartoon strips, posters, illustrations, films —are a substitute for the written word is another topic.)

Apart from educational level, what you find in low economic levels is that people have more urgent needs, more basic, primary needs. You know the old saying, "Don't send missionaries to hungry people." You don't talk about feeding problems to the parents of children who are not getting enough to eat, or about good sleep habits for children who are sleeping seven in a bed. Abraham Maslow's illuminating analysis of the hierarchy of needs and his principle of prepotent needs are relevant here: that is, that the most basic needs must be satisfied first (such as food and safety) before the organism can move on to the satisfaction of higher needs (such as response, love, creativeness).

With respect to target groups, it is important to be aware of the qualities of the group likely to improve the effectiveness of mental health education. One is the desirability of having "homogeneous, highly motivated groups"; and the other is the importance of "populations at special risk." Since the topic of "homogeneous, highly motivated groups" has already been discussed, it may seem repetitious to bring it up again. The reason is that no principle is more basic in classifying target groups, and vast amounts of effort are wasted when that principle is ignored. There is, of course, a time and a place for the heterogeneous group—the one-night stand, the broadside. But in the planning of a total program, it will always pay to think in terms of homogeneous groups: groups that are homogeneous with respect to their needs, their problems, their goals, their plans, their intentions, their longings, insofar as these can properly be placed in a mental health context.

"Populations at special risk" is a good public health term and more than a little jargonish but highly applicable in mental health education, especially when tied in with the concept of "crisis intervention." Eric Lindemann's definition of "crisis" is "a situation in which a population or group is exposed to a hazard which taxes their emotional resources" (2). Crises may be circumstantial, such as in a catastrophe, separation, handicap; or developmental, as in growth and transition, such as to school, college, marriage, a new job, or retirement. All such "populations" are likely to be better "targets" for mental health education than are undefined, scattered, miscellaneous, or unmotivated groups.

PLANNING THE MATERIALS

Now to move on to the topic of planning materials: selection, use, building programs around materials, and the sometimes knotty question of whether to try to develop your own material.

SELECTION

Here comes another of those platitudes that nevertheless must be stated. *Select good materials.* This must be stressed because so many bad materials keep on being selected. It is discouraging to discover how many programs use materials that are incontrovertibly inferior. But of course in order to select good things, you have to be informed about what is available. It is one of the tenets of this book that anybody who has a job with "mental health" in the title has a solemn obligation to know something about mental health: about what material is

available and about how to differentiate between good and bad
material.

USE

Second, *use your materials*. That is another platitude that
may sound a little silly, but the people who go out in the field
to visit mental health programs are constantly coming across
great quantities of good materials that are not being used.
Sometimes that is because the materials have somehow landed
in the wrong department of an organization, whereas if they
were in another department they might be used to advantage.
What happens again and again in large organizations is that
one division or bureau or department has the budget, buys the
materials, and then does not know what to do with them, while
another department is dying to have them but has no funds,
does not know they are available across the hall—and never
the twain shall meet. If you work in a large organization, a
few inquiries about what is available in other departments
may turn up an occasional gold mine.

Use materials *thoughtfully and selectively*. Do not use them
just because "they're there," or because your predecessor used
them, or because "they're free." Let your imagination run. If
you think an item is good, you do not have to set up a brain-
storming session in order to stop to think "What would be a
good way to use this? How have others used it? How can we
take advantage of their experience?"

Use them *systematically and intensively*. This is another of
Dr. Loyd Rowland's ideas related to his emphasis on homogeneous, highly motivated groups. He is very persuasive about
the desirability of using material and techniques intensively
and systematically, to the point of saturation. For instance,
Pierre the Pelican, in the way in which Dr. Rowland originally
conceived it, is an example of saturation usage. It went to *all*
parents of first-borns in a state. Thus you achieve saturation
of one population, and as he says, if you gradually reach one
population after another, eventually you reach all the people.
He did a series on *Milestones to Maturity* (22) which he has

tried to have distributed to *all* high school students in a school system. That is a standard public health technique applied to mental health: to pick out a special population and do a saturation job. Dr. Rowland likes to see his police films (23) go to *all* the police in a given community, and also be incorporated in the Training Manual of the Police Department. Therefore, the use of the films would not depend on their being promoted by some outside group, such as a mental health association. Once a film is in the Manual, it is there for generations (so they say) and will automatically turn up at a certain point in the training program—an excellent system.

One of the popular GAP reports—popular in the sense of being well-liked and in great demand—has been the report *Mental Retardation: A Family Crisis* (14). Some agencies have made it available to *all* physicians in a given geographic locality. Edith Stern's splendid booklet *Mental Illness: A Guide for the Family* (24) is the kind of thing that ought to be given to *all* families of first admissions to mental hospitals. That again would be an example of the saturation method.

Dr. Rowland likes to remind us that when we are dealing with material for parents of children of a given age, we have to repeat it with each new parent population. We sometimes tend to get tired of our own materials and think that a given piece has been used too long and we need something new. That may be true, but it is also important to remember that new generations of consumers are coming along all the time, and you have not done a saturation job unless you reach the newcomers.

BUILDING PROGRAM FROM MATERIALS

Which comes first, the program or the material? You might say that ideally the program should come first, but certainly that need not always be the case. It can work either way. There are some outstanding instances in which an organization has first defined its program sharply and then developed materials around the program. But that process is reversible. Somebody else will come along and see those same materials

—a film, for instance, or a set of plays or pamphlets—and will then get some new ideas for developing program around materials. Some mental health agencies have adopted the excellent idea of putting on an occasional "Showcase" in which the purpose is to give people in other community agencies an idea of what is available in the way of good mental health materials; then these people go back to their own organizations and develop program around the new materials. The same thing happens with dramatic sketches. When people see how easy it is to use the *Plays for Living*, they often build program around plays. That was done extensively in connection with the play *My Name Is Legion* (25), by Nora Stirling and Nina Ridenour, an hour-long dramatization of the life of Clifford Beers. Many state and local mental health associations built portions of their program around that play, using it for a combination of education, public relations, and fund-raising.

Thus on the question of the relation between program and materials, opportunism has a place. If a particularly good piece of material turns up, grab it and fit it into program, though always within a logical and established framework, or else the old enemy discursiveness may trip you up.

DEVELOPMENT OF NEW MATERIALS

Do you develop your own materials or do you use other people's? There are times when it is not easy to decide which is better. Suppose you have a program idea: you look over what materials you can find—they do not exactly suit your purposes —so you weigh the possibility of preparing your own. Is it a good idea to produce your own? There are pros, and there are cons.

On the pro side, there is the point that if you develop your own, you may well be closer to the immediate needs of your group. That is one of the reasons why it is a policy of the Extension Service of the Department of Agriculture to encourage their specialists and county agents to develop their own materials, on the theory that they will then be more closely in touch with the people they are trying to serve. Another reason for preparing one's own material is that it may be cheaper, which is sometimes a compelling reason. On this point, however, inspect costs carefully because you can be fooled if you don't. Mimeographing, for instance, may prove to be more expensive than printing; or material you produce on a small scale may cost more than something you buy that has been produced on a large scale. Another reason for developing your own materials is that the process can be excellent experience for the group that does the work.

On the con side—that is, against the development of your own material—is the fact that much material prepared by inexperienced people turns out to be amateurish if not outright bad. By the time a group has worked hard on it for weeks or months and tried to satisfy everybody, they tend to lose their perspective, and may not realize how poor the final product is.

Another problem that may not be recognized until it is too late is how time-consuming it is to prepare your own material. It takes an incredible amount of time to do a decent job. It also requires a great deal of skill, more than is ordinarily realized. Because people often want what they think of as simple material, they think it will be simple to develop. Actually the correlation is likely to be in the other direction: the simpler it is the harder it is to develop.

If you are in the business of mental health education, it will be important for you to be acquainted with the principal sources of information. You will want to follow at least the principal journals. If you do not have time to read as many of the articles as you would like, at least make a practice of running your eye down the bibliographies in order to notice what items turn up repeatedly, for that often means that others have found them valuable. Also watch for announcements of various kinds and request publications catalogs of agencies and organizations. Many of them have low-cost publications or newsletters which can be useful sources of information. Some maintain lists to which your name may be added on request.

A final point that is relevant if you are trying to decide whether or not to develop your own materials is the question of competence—exactly the same point that was dealt with earlier in this chapter under the topic of criteria for decision in defining program. Does your organization have the competence? If you do not have it, can you develop it? Or can you mobilize it? Perhaps it is there in your community but you have to ferret it out and pull it together. If somebody in your group has a great urge to write, let him write. In fact, urge him to write, support him, encourage him. That is the way writers are developed. Do not assume, however, that just because somebody *wants* to write he will be good at it, especially at first. But do give him his head. Some of the best writers on mental health today are people who started without any particular training but with a strong urge to write in the field. It is a great joy to watch a writer grow. Sometimes their motivation stems from personal problems and experiences—perhaps from having been a mental patient or from a family tragedy. When the motivation is strong, such people can contribute importantly.

In summary then: do not assume a writer is a writer is a writer, but do try to make use of talent or desire among your own group. Do not underestimate the difficulties, because great skill is required to produce good material, but do not be afraid to go ahead if you are pretty clear about what you want and what is involved. Do not leap too quickly to the conclusion that there is nothing to fit your needs unless you have studied available resources thoroughly. Keep your eyes and your mind open and you may be surprised how much comes your way, both in materials and program ideas.

5

The Mental Health Effort: An Overview

"HOW ARE WE DOING?"

So far these chapters have been concerned with mental health education. Now it seems a good idea to place the education effort in larger context, and examine the mental health effort as a whole, with special attention to the changes that have been taking place and a hard look at the knotty question of progress.

PERSPECTIVE

My involvement in mental health goes back to the middle 1920's, in those days called mental hygiene. If you have cared about a field for that many years you have inevitably done a lot of pondering. One of the advantages of growing older is your comfortable conviction that you have a better perspective than you used to. You can recognize patterns and repetitions of patterns not discernible to your younger associates. You have seen well-meaning effort, prodigious effort, which you can now look back upon as having been wasted, or worse, as having been in the wrong direction. Sometimes you are overwhelmed by the sense of déjà vu . . . seen-before . . . this-is-where-I-came-in . . . the "here-we-go-*again*" feeling. You can now identify the Messianic complex that you and your colleagues shared in earlier years and that seems to afflict many of the devotees of the behavioral sciences. You have learned to be a good deal more cautious about the easy over-confidence, the fruitless optimism that stem from excesses of zeal and wishfulness and unrealistic ideals.

Out of all this comes one firm determination above all: *You don't want to be fooled.* You want to know whether we are or are not making headway. You want to know which types of effort are working and which are not. You want to differentiate, and you want others to differentiate, between action and talk about action; between ideas and verbiage; between good ideas and half-baked ones. You are unwilling to jump on the bandwagon of the fashionable new emphasis of the moment, intolerant of extravagant promises and pronouncements. You are no longer taken in by mere newness, because you have learned the hard way that there is no value in newness for its own sake. And the same is true of change. You are suspicious of ideas or activities glibly labeled progress until you have had a chance to examine the direction in which they are moving, because you now know how easy it is to mistake mere change for progress.

As part of this examining—weighing—judging process, you have learned respect for the existential facts. You want to face up to things as they are.

ASSESSMENT OF STATUS

That is why I now wish to devote a few pages here to an assessment that might be called "How are we doing in the mental health program?"—which I quickly qualify by adding ". . . as I see it."

When I was Director of Education at the National Association for Mental Health in the late 1940's and early 1950's (National Committee for Mental Hygiene prior to 1950), we used to struggle with the problem of how to describe in a few phrases meaningful to the general public the sweep of activities we envisioned in a fully functioning mental health program. People seemed to find it difficult to grasp the scope of needs as we saw them. Therefore, we were happy to borrow a gimmick from our friends in the Canadian Mental Health Association. They had hit upon a simple acrostic they called REST to describe program structure:

R esearch
E ducation
S ervices
T raining

(In fact the Canadians had some fun carrying this one step farther and calling it "Rest in Peace"—the "in" standing for international activities and the "Peace" being an ultimate goal all would agree on.)

As used here Training refers to professional training, both academic and in-service, including mental health incorporated into professional education as part of the training in the skills of the specific profession. Education refers to mental health education of the public including mental health education of professional groups apart from their own professional training.

So now I would like to comment on how I feel about what is happening in these four program areas: Research, Education, Services, Training, not making any attempt to cover the whole picture, just hitting a few high spots and well aware that some of my most respected colleagues will not agree with some of my points.

Inspection of these four program areas reveals at once that all four have increased greatly in amount of activity. An example is seen in the National Institute of Mental Health budget, which covers all four areas and which has gone from a few million dollars annually in the late 1940's, when NIMH was created, to a figure that may reach $400,000,000 or something close to that before these pages are off the press (1969). Among other things this reflects a growth in public support of mental health activities across the board.

An increase in the amount of research is evidenced by the number of books, journals, professional meetings, projects, and funds devoted to research when compared with, say, twenty years ago. Increase in public education is similarly apparent in the number of books, journals, and meetings devoted to it and in the handling of the subject by the popular press and other forms of the mass media.

As to services, there has been a significant growth both in inpatient and outpatient services but particularly outpatient, of which the development of community health centers is but one example. An increase in the amount and number of trained personnel is reflected in many different ways, for instance in the membership of the two APA's: the American Psychiatric Association, which has doubled nearly every decade since 1900, totaling over 15,000 in 1968; and the American Psychological Association, which now boasts the astronomical membership figure of 25,000.

Clearly then, the mental health effort can report expansion of activities in these four areas. In earlier days those of us who were identified with the mental health movement would have been gratified to see all this stepped-up activity. But of course activity is merely a means to an end and not an end in itself. One must ask to what extent the increased activity is resulting in progress toward the basic mental health objectives of treatment and prevention. Does increased activity also mean increased effectiveness? Is *more* accompanied by *better*? For instance, are more people getting better treatment? For it can happen, and sometimes does, that though more services are available, fewer people are getting them and that the services may even be worse rather than better. True, increase in the amount of service or in any of the other program areas is *likely* to mean better, but one cannot take this for granted. Therefore it is necessary to examine increases from the point of view of progress toward goals—a good way of taking one's bearings now and then.

Just as a casual inspection of the four program areas shows that activity is unquestionably increasing in quantity, similar inspection suggests that results may be quite uneven in their effectiveness in the same four areas. It is necessary to look at them one by one.

RESEARCH

In previous chapters I have not tried to conceal my personal doubts about the value of a great deal of the research in mental disorders that is going on. How much truly significant new knowledge is emerging from the vast research effort? Sometimes when I see what goes into research and then what comes out, I cannot help wondering just what it all adds up to. If that is heresy so be it. My own mind is full of questions.

Despite my lack of enthusiasm for much of the behavioral research I have more of a feeling of excitement about the progress in biochemical research in schizophrenia. Although anything resembling a scientific evaluation of this type of research is beyond my technical competence, the optimism of some of my more qualified associates has brushed off on me and I share their hopes that the long awaited "break-through" may come from that direction and that progress is genuine.

About the results of many other types of research, I feel less sanguine. Epidemiology is an example of a research field that for years has been dangling exciting promises for new insights into mental illness, but somehow the clues it offers never seem to get fully explored and so just keep on dangling. Results of research in mental health education are disappointing, possibly because not enough systematic effort has been devoted to breaking down objectives into manageable units. Evaluative studies in administration have been fruitful in the improvement of services in specific instances though they can scarcely be expected to penetrate very far into etiology or prevention. In short, I have a sense of disappointment in research results to date with the possible exception of some of the organic approaches to schizophrenia. And even those are more in the realm of hope than actuality.

EDUCATION

As mentioned above, education as used here refers to education of the public, not professional training. When it comes to education *about* mental illness, we can take a lot of satisfaction in the results. There is ample evidence of real change in attitude on the part of the public in their understanding of what mental illness is and their willingness to support efforts on behalf of the mentally ill (4). Compared with thirty years ago, or even twenty, the changes are gratifying beyond what one would have dared hope. Like almost everything else in the mental health effort, it is impossible to "prove" how much of this has come about as a result of mental health education, but I myself am convinced that a sizable portion is traceable to the total education push.

But when it comes to education *for* mental health, that is another story. Some of the difficulties of assessing mental health education have already been discussed in the chapter on evaluation. Quite possibly it is the hardest of all the program areas to evaluate, so I shall leave it with a reaffirmation of my own faith in its potential. Although it is impossible to prove effectiveness on a large scale for the nation or the culture as a whole, a strong case can be made for its value with specific groups and individuals under specific circumstances. On that point my conviction never wavers. Nor do I waver in my conviction that the potential in mental health education is enormous and if properly structured can play a vital role in "the welfare of mankind." I say this while remaining fully sensitive to how much is wrong with it as it functions today. We *know* better than we *do*. And a great deal—a very great deal—can be done to improve its effectiveness.

SERVICES

Services can be divided roughly into inpatient care and outpatient care. The quality of care of patients in mental hospitals has unquestionably improved in many places in recent years, though only once in a while is the improvement as dramatic as occasional journalists enjoy depicting in the popular press when they have discovered some institution that has been remodeled and they would like to have their readers think that such changes are now typical. Too often they are not typical at all and there are tragic instances of ghastly neglect and mismanagement that sound more like the eighteenth than the twentieth century, except that they are still going on now in the twentieth century. But happily those are not typical either. The truth seems to lie in between. There are many places where there has been no perceptible improvement at all; others where there have been flurries of improvement that later disappeared; and a few where the improvement has been dramatic and apparently lasting. Also in some places there has been imaginative development of a variety of types of ambulatory service as a substitute for twenty-four hour care, though this development too is spotty. In other words, improvement seems to be uneven, but by and large, for the country as a whole, there has almost surely been definite progress in most aspects of inpatient care.

As to improvement in outpatient care: clinics, schools, health and social agencies, private therapy—that is more debatable, although as stressed above, the *amount* of psychiatric service has increased enormously. Has there been commensurate improvement in quality? Or, in fact, has there been any perceptible improvement at all? I am not sure there has been. I hope I am wrong.

The picture is a little different with respect to services for the mentally retarded, which seem for the time being to be improving. The retarded have always been neglected but recognition of their needs has received new impetus in the last few years. It is too soon to see how far-reaching the new efforts will be, or how lasting, but there again one can hope.

There was a day long ago when many of us naïvely thought that our problems of providing "treatment for all who need it" would be solved when we had more of everything: more clinical facilities, more trained personnel, more money, more community support. But now we are more realistic in recognizing that mental health manpower will never catch up with need. We are also more realistic in recognizing the inadequacies of the traditional clinical model, the therapeutic dyad: one therapist, one patient, face to face. Consequently there is now much earnest, constructive searching for more adequate models in therapy, in prevention, and in education.

A number of the new models are coming from public health. Some of the public health concepts, having particular significance for mental health are: levels of prevention with emphasis on primary prevention; crisis intervention; populations at special risk; and epidemiology. Most of these have already been commented on in previous chapters.

TRAINING

When it comes to the professional training of the core professions—therapists and those responsible for the care of the mentally ill, chiefly psychiatrists, clinical psychologists, social workers, nurses, and psychiatric attendants—it seems logical to assume that if there had been any striking improvement in the quality of professional training in recent years by comparison with thirty years ago, it would surely be apparent in a number of different ways and would also be reflected in the quality of patient care. Are there significant changes of these kinds? If so, they are not very clear.

When it comes to mental health training in the other helping professions, that is, the incorporation of mental health concepts in the professional training of groups other than the core professions—that seems more satisfactory. There are many signs that mental health ideas are being well absorbed by other professional groups such as teachers, clergymen, public health nurses, and group workers, to name a few.

SPOTCHECK OF PROGRESS

In summary then, in my personal spotcheck of progress, I would say that the things I feel best about are improvement in the care of mental patients in hospitals; increased public awareness of the problems of mental illness and mental retardation; and integration of mental health concepts into the other helping professions.

I feel optimistic about the prospect of an eventual breakthrough in schizophrenia, even while recognizing that this is more in the realm of hope than reality and that no time schedule can yet be assigned. I also feel hopeful that from now on more attention is going to be paid to the needs of the mentally retarded.

I never lose confidence in the *potential* of mental health education, though I feel painfully dissatisfied with the way it is being conducted. I would not argue that it is possible to demonstrate proof of effectiveness in education for mental health in the population as a whole, but I would argue vociferously that it is highly effective in individual cases and with specific groups.

I feel many doubts about what is being produced in the name of research, and am still looking for evidence of improvement in professional skills. I see only limited progress in understanding of the origin and prevention of the major mental illnesses; and no evidence at all of a decrease in incidence and prevalence of mental and emotional disorders including the neuroses and other forms of aberrant and undesirable behavior.

Most of all I feel disappointed that the mental health effort has not made more of an impact on the vast array of personal and social problems about which it has been concerned: family and other interpersonal disharmonies; neurotic suffering, tension, anxiety, and the myriad forms of personal discomfort and inadequacy; standards of social behavior, morality, and responsibility; and man's inhumanity to man.

INTERFERENCES

As I have said repeatedly in these pages, there is much that can be done to improve the effectiveness of the mental health

effort. To that end, there are certain rough spots in our thinking that should be dealt with. Two of these have been touched
on in previous chapters, but need further discussion because
they should be taken seriously. The first is the ambiguity of
the term mental health and the second is the amount of fuzzy
thinking that goes on in the field.

AMBIGUITY

Mental health is an ambiguous term and nothing is going to
change that fact. Ambiguity is inherent in the concept. Recognizing this will not solve it but should help keep us from getting trapped by it.

The ambiguity does have some positive value in that the resulting diversity accounts in part for the richness of the field.
If you trace the history of the concepts behind the terms—as
I have done to some extent in my book *Mental Health in the
United States: A Fifty-Year History* (9)—you see how they
arose and what purpose they were trying to fulfill. And they
still are fulfilling certain purposes, important ones. But even
so, on the whole the extreme ambiguity of the term is regrettable and not a matter to be ignored. (Not a matter for emula-
tion, either, I might add. For now the terms "human potential" and "the human potentiality movement" are coming into
use and about to fall into exactly the same ambiguity trap the
mental health movement has suffered from.)

One thing that might help a little would be for people to be
more careful about terminology. For instance, the terms "the
mentally ill" and "mental illness" are used much too loosely.
When you hear such statements as "Twenty million Americans
are mentally ill," that means that the words "mentally ill" are
being used to cover some vague amorphous scatter of mental
and emotional disturbances completely impossible of definition.

It is better for the term "mental illness" to be restricted to
those disabling or incapacitating mental and emotional disturbances severe enough to require treatment by a psychiatrist
or comparable therapist, usually in a hospital. "Mental illness"

should not be applied to the garden varieties of unhappiness or maladjustment or reactive upset unless these are of such type or degree as to cause serious impairment in functioning. Some combination of terms like "mental and emotional disturbances" or "mental and emotional disorders" (awkward, but the best we have at the moment) should be used for the wide range of disorders which, though often too severe to be called "minor," are nevertheless not as fully incapacitating as psychoses.

It can be confusing when "mental health" and "mental illness" are used as if they were synonyms. That gets us into some funny jams, like the article on "The Prevention of Mental Health" and the speaker who urged his audience to "fight this terrible battle against mental health." Although frequently done, it seems debatable whether it is a good idea to use mental *health* to describe *treatment* services to the mentally *ill*. For instance, why "mental health pavilion" as the name of the psychiatric unit in a general hospital? What's the matter with the word "psychiatric"? Psychiatric department, psychiatric division, psychiatric clinic, psychiatric hospital. Those are good words. Sol W. Ginsburg, in his excellent book *A Psychiatrist's Views on Social Issues* (5), made a strong point of this. To use "mental health" as a euphemism when one means "mental illness" *specifically* is pandering to the type of fear and prejudice the mental *hygiene* effort has been trying to combat.

Though the use of mental health to mean mental illness can be challenged, it would be hard to get along without mental health as an over-all term. Mental health field, mental health movement, mental health effort, mental health problem, mental health department, mental health education, mental health literature, mental health association—each of those is useful in its place. Also mental health when applied to primary prevention, to keep mental illness from developing—that too is permissible. "Mental health worker" is awkward. "Mental health educator" has a certain disadvantage, because it seems better to have the name that is applied to a professional *person* reflect his training rather than what he *does*. Whether mental health education ever will, or whether it should, develop into an actual profession is one of the moot questions I would rather not get involved in. I can argue on either side, though I am inclined to feel resistant to the idea partly because of the ambiguities already discussed, but chiefly because mental health education is a *process* to which many disciplines contribute, and not a specific discipline based on specific techniques.

Now about my hopes and wishes for the future of mental health education. I would like to see the time come when we could eliminate both the words and the idea. I am in no hurry. I do not want to eliminate them now, or in the lifetime of even the youngest of my colleagues. I am thinking far ahead—not only beyond 1984, maybe beyond 2084. I would like to think that we are working toward the point where everything having to do with mental health is so completely integrated into other activities that we would have no further use for the concept. I would like to think that those of us concerned with mental health education were gradually working ourselves out of a job, or more accurately, working our successors out of a job, because mental health education would be integrated into *all* education and all cognate activities, such as child-rearing. We (they!) would not talk about mental health in parent education because that would just be *good* parent education; or about mental health in teacher training because *good* teacher training would take care of that. We could discard the barbarous term "psychiatric pediatrics" because there would be only one kind of pediatrics: *good* pediatrics. We would not have to talk about mental health in public health because mental health would be incorporated in *all* relevant aspects of public health. One of my hopes would be that by then medicine would have rediscovered the individual, the lost "total person," and that the dreadful fractionation that now causes so much needless suffering will be looked back upon with horror as one of the regrettable defects of our present era. But until that happy day comes somebody has got to carry the torch, and keep us reminded that man's feeling-side can be neglected only at terrible cost.

FUZZY THINKING

On the point of fuzzy thinking I am distressed by some of the naïveté, the wishfulness, the lack of realism, the lack of plain thoughtfulness in the literature because I think it is responsible for the ineffectiveness of many aspects of the mental health effort. For instance, a professional person, an officer of one of our largest professional associations, recently made this statement in one of our respected journals: "Mental health used to mean its opposite—mental disease. Now it means not just health but human well-being." I maintain that *that* is precisely the type of formulation that generates confusion. If mental health means human well-being, who does what? What education and experience should be required of those who work in the mental health field? How is responsibility apportioned? What is my job and what is yours and who decides?

An example of this is the demand that psychiatrists, psychologists, and other representatives of the core professions in mental health become social planners—which is fine up to a point. But to establish that point requires some hard and realistic thinking. Needless to say, I am well aware of today's trends toward "community psychiatry" and toward developing a subprofession of "the" community psychiatrist who will presumably have had special training in the community aspects of preventive psychiatry. Using "psychiatry" here in a generic sense to include clinical psychology and cognate fields, I am more than eager to support any effort that will spread the insights of psychiatry more widely. I am glad to see psychiatrists and their associates becoming more community-conscious and taking more community responsibility. But this trend can go only so far. When it goes too far new problems develop. There can be as much loss and confusion if these groups spread themselves too thin as if they remain too aloof. There is no less danger in the ivory tower than in the pressures on psychiatrists and social scientists to be all-things-to-all-people. Professional people in the medical, social, and behavioral sciences are limited in their time, their energy, their experience, their ability, their understanding—just like all other human beings. They are often not qualified to cope with certain types of demands put upon them and may even be particularly unqualified because there is a selective factor in their very choice of a profession. One of the tasks ahead will be how to use psychiatrists and their associates wisely, neither demanding miracles of them, nor overlooking the body of knowledge they can bring to bear on the problems of the present scene.

Related to this question of what can be fairly expected of psychiatry, another troublesome matter is the amount of exaggeration that seems to be floating around in both the public and the professional press. A lot of it occurs in connection with the subject of mental retardation, which is so much in the air these days. Here is an example, a statement by the same person who made the comment about human well-being quoted above. In speaking of mental retardation he said, "It is hard to think of a human affliction as amenable to productive intervention." Now that is sheer hyperbole. It is true we have not had nearly enough intervention, and it is good to see more steam behind the intervention drive. But such exaggerated statements as this are to be deplored for many reasons, including the unwarranted hopes they build in the minds of families of retardates.

Reports of research results in mental retardation also seem strangely subject to exaggeration. Some bits and pieces of new knowledge about the prevention of birth injuries and specific physiological disorders are encouraging, but even those often get blown up in the reporting, especially from the point of view of percentages of cases likely to benefit from the new discovery. Scientists themselves, more often than not, state their research results conservatively. It is when results are reported in the mass media that inflation takes over. This is no favor to the public. Promising more than can be delivered is a form of intellectual dishonesty, even though it is not intended as such, and in the long run is as disruptive as any other form of dishonesty.

So much for the two topics—ambiguity and fuzzy thinking. I could give many more examples of unnecessary confusion, looseness, inaccuracy, lack of realism, but my purpose will have been served if I flag the tendency for attention.

6

Mental Health and the Human Potentiality

"WHAT COMES NEXT?"

Historically the mental health effort had its roots in concern
for mentally ill people. This quickly developed into concern for
the prevention of mental illness, which in turn soon broad-
ened out to include interest in mental health in all its ramifi-
cations. Thus these two interests, the one focusing chiefly on
mental illness, the other more on mental health, have been
marching side by side, supplementing and necessary to each
other, a proper and a useful team.

But now a new line of march seems to be shaping up based
on new interests and new emphases that will supplement
and extend the older interests just as they have been supplementing each other. The new emphases do not have a name
yet, and maybe never will—nor do I propose to try to give
them one here. I prefer to use such terms as shifting emphases,
changing concepts, new approaches and techniques.

Some readers may challenge the relevance for mental health
education of some of the "far out" topics and points of view
to be discussed in this chapter. I feel strongly, however, that

they are not only relevant but absolutely *basic* to the development of a viable concept of mental health. I see the new emphases as an extrapolation of the mental illness-mental health continuum, a natural and desirable extension of the mental health ideal. These new ideas are already having an impact on the mental health effort, both in therapy and in education, and are likely to have a great deal more impact in the future. In fact so important do I consider these new emphases that I will go so far as to say that no discussion of mental health education today is complete without some recognition of these burgeoning ideas and their implications.

After all, the success of any education effort depends in the long run on the validity of its concepts. Education can be constructive only if soundly based on sound ideas. Mental health education attempts to inculcate certain assumptions and convictions about the nature of man. But if more sophisticated, more soundly conceived ideas are emerging, ideas that are beginning to form a basis for a more valid science of man, then what could be more relevant for mental health education and indeed for the entire mental health effort?

I feel greatly encouraged by some of the new ideas. Some fresh breezes are blowing. I feel an excitement in the air I have not felt for many years. What is impressive is that these new ideas are coming from *many* different directions. More than that they are coming *together:* re-enforcing and enriching each other and demonstrating remarkable consistency in their basic point of view. To describe them in enough detail to make them come alive would require a full book. In a few paragraphs, however, I shall try to touch some of the high spots—lumping together the sources, the emerging ideas, and the techniques. These various concepts and approaches do not fall into neat independent categories. They overlap and interweave and relate to each other in ways that could be examined from half a hundred different angles. In this short space I can do no more than chart a few trends. Here is a list offered not as comprehensive coverage of this growing new philosophy but rather as a rough map of where the ideas are coming from.

SOURCES OF THE NEW EMPHASES

- Humanistic Psychology (Third Force)
- Non-Traditional Therapies and Group Techniques
- Parapsychology (psychical research)
- Comparative Religion and Philosophy
- Explorations in the Human Potentiality

HUMANISTIC PSYCHOLOGY (Third Force)

One of the most important sources of the new ideas is the more dynamic subdivisions of organized professional psychology concerned with human experience and open to concepts flowing in from other disciplines. Although "Humanistic Psychology" and "Third Force" are not exactly synonyms, they are often used interchangeably. I like the term Third Force because the very words imply that it is possible to understand the *Third* Force only against a background of the other two forces and I think that some grasp of all three is essential to an understanding of the status of the new psychology.

Recently I came across a paragraph that summarized in remarkably few words the orientation of the three forces. It was in an article by Carl Rogers entitled "Towards a Science of the Person" in the *Journal of Humanistic Psychology* (45). Rogers says:

I share with Maslow and others the view that there are three broad emphases in American psychology. These resemble three ocean currents flowing side by side, mingling, with no clear line of demarcation, yet definitely different nonetheless. Like the flotsam and jetsam which floats on each ocean current, certain words and phrases identify, even though they do not define, the separate flowing trends. Associated with the first trend are terms such as *behaviorism, objective, experimental, impersonal, logical positivistic, operational, laboratory*. Associated with the second current are terms such as *Freudian, neo-Freudian, psychoanalytic, psychology of the unconscious, instinctual, ego-psychology, id-psychology, dynamic psychology.* Associated with the third are terms such as *phenomenological, existential, self-theory, self-actualization, health-and-growth psychology, being and becoming, science and inner experience.*

An excellent paragraph! Then to each of those three categories I would add a few more words. To the first I would add *methodology, research design, control group, replication,* and a whole dictionary of statistical terms. To the second I would add *psychopathology, psychotherapy, depth psychology, interpersonal relationships,* and several pages from the psychiatric glossary. The third might include such terms as *wholeness* and the *whole person, human potentiality, awareness, consciousness, expanded awareness* and *expanded consciousness,* and many references to different kinds of direct personal subjective experience such as *religious experience, creative experience,* and Maslow's valuable term *"peak experience."*

Each of the first two forces has certain weaknesses and certain strengths that are now fairly apparent though they were less so a few years back. The major weakness of the first force, the behavioristic-experimental-positivistic approach, is its slavish adherence to the quantitative and fragmenting methods of the physical sciences. Its strength is that it has produced a methodology that provides the best safeguards yet developed to insure us against fooling ourselves.

A weakness of the second force, the Freudian-psychiatric-psychoanalytic, is its too casual reliance on untested hypotheses and its heavy illness-orientation with too much of its theory drawn from pathology and not enough from observation of the forces of health and growth. Its strengths—and they are great indeed—lie in the depth and richness it has brought to the understanding of the dynamics of human behavior, especially its elucidation of unconscious mechanisms and the rationales of motivation.

What delights me about the Third Force is that it is not tearing down: *it is building up.* It is building *onto* the contributions of the other two forces. It is deriving from the other two forces that which is best, utilizing their strengths, trying not to be trapped by their weaknesses. Leaders of the Third Force—men like Gardner Murphy, Abraham Maslow, Carl Rogers, to name just three—are well trained in the exact sciences. They know how to set up a hypothesis, how to test it, how to create an elegant research design. They move about freely in formal methodology and statistics. But they are also soundly oriented in psychiatric and psychoanalytic theory and depth psychology. Many of them are or have been therapists.

The Third Force is a sophisticated approach, not a field for amateurs or dabblers. At its best it is a coalescence, an integration of forces. It does not deny previous values, as new "schools" of thought often delight in doing, but tries to utilize the old values while at the same time assessing and correcting errors and faulty emphases of the past. If observed phenomena do not fit the existing theoretical structure, the Third Force does not toss out the phenomena—as traditional approaches tend to do—but re-examines the structure, modifies it, or if necessary reconstructs it entirely. Instead of the closed systems that are the earmark of the other two forces, the strength of the Third Force is its openness, its inclusiveness.

The American Association for Humanistic Psychology describes the humanistic orientation as focusing on the experiencing *person* and thus on *experience* as the primary phenomenon in the study of man; and as emphasizing such distinctively human qualities as choice, creativeness, values, and self-realization rather than mechanistic and reductionist approaches. Knowing full well that all "ways of knowing" are fallible, the Third Force does not look upon "science" as a rigid, to-be-worshipped body of established facts, but rather concerns itself with "scientific" as a method of trying to find out, a way of tackling problems, one way of knowing.

Some of the most interesting ideas in this general area are those of Abraham Maslow who, in my opinion, is the most important conceptualizer we have had since William James. Maslow has given us a whole new glossary of meaningful terms: peak experience, self-actualization, hierarchy of needs, deficiency motivation, B-cognition ("B" for "Being"), B-love, B-values, sacralization and desacralization of science, to name

a few. As one of the leaders of the Third Force and the
Humanistic group, he is concerned with the integration of a
health-and-growth psychology with psychopathology and the
dynamics stemming from psychoanalytic theory. "Science,"
he says, "does not need to abdicate from the problems of love,
creativeness, value, beauty, imagination, ethics, joy." The core
of all his work is the study of man in his "full humanness."
He has published voluminously (37, 38, 39, 40).

NON-TRADITIONAL THERAPIES
AND GROUP TECHNIQUES

Ever since the early days of Freud, "schools" of psychotherapy have been splitting off, forming and reforming, and
they still are. Some of the newer and less orthodox therapies
have names that are more or less self-explanatory such as
the nondirective, client-centered therapy of Rogers, Gestalt
therapy, existentialist therapy, and the variety of family
therapies. Many of these are eclectic, borrowing freely from
older traditions and from each other, not relying exclusively
on any one school of thought. Many of them seem tougher
than the psychoanalytic tradition in placing responsibility
on the patient for utilizing his own resources in the healing
process; and they seem more sensitive to interrelationship—
the relations between therapist and patient in the clinical
dyad and the interrelations among participants in the group
setting. They encourage focusing on the feelings of the present
moment rather than scanning those of the past as do the
more orthodox therapies.

Group methods seem to be more in evidence than heretofore,
often loosely called T-groups (T for Training, stemming
from the techniques developed by the National Training Laboratory, best known for its summer sessions in Bethel, Maine).
Originally T-group denoted a fairly specific technique, but it
is now being used as a convenient term to cover an increasing
variety of methods and group structures. Although some T-
groups are intended as primarily therapeutic, many are designed less for persons seeking to solve personal problems than

for "normal" people who wish an experience in personal growth and interrelations. They include a wide range of techniques such as the confrontation or basic encounter group, which may utilize an intensive stress situation (for instance, marathon or round-the-clock sessions) to encourage the participant to recognize and come to terms with his feelings "here-and-now"; leaderless groups; self-help groups, of which Alcoholics Anonymous and Synanon (for drug addicts) are examples; techniques developed for the training of business executives, for the development of body and sensory awareness, and for the enhancement of creativity.

The growth of group techniques is going to be an interesting phenomenon to watch. Some of the methods of some of the leaders would make a clinician shudder. Some of them sound like a quaint combination of the masochistic and the sadistic. Some are referred to half jokingly as "instant analysis" or "instant enlightenment"—in the hands of "young men in a hurry." Nevertheless some of these new techniques are imaginative, sophisticated, altogether challenging. They *must* be taken seriously by traditional therapy and education.

PARAPSYCHOLOGY (Psychical Research)

Psi phenomena—nonphysical factors and processes—do not fit the traditional framework of perception and cognition. Among the principal categories are: extrasensory perception (ESP), which includes clairvoyance, telepathy, and precognition; and psychokinesis (PK), meaning direct influence exerted on a physical system independently of physical instrumentation. Examples of processes that may partake of ESP and PK include mental healing, dowsing, automatisms, trance phenomena, and many forms of nonsensory perception and cognition.

Now these are *observed phenomena*. They *are*. They *exist*. And anybody who says they do not exist is positively not informed. It is as simple as that. These phenomena have been demonstrated beyond any reasonable cavil. The supporting scientific evidence is fully as sound as the evidence for a great many physical phenomena that individuals do not have a chance to verify for themselves. Parapsychology is now fully established as a recognized and incontrovertible body of scientific knowledge and as a scientific method utilizing rigorous traditional scientific techniques to verify its findings and extend its boundaries. It is nothing short of preposterous that these subjects have been so neglected in our universities, subject to so much opprobrium and emotionalism from serious scientists, and allowed to remain in such a state of chaos that interested lay people (and they are legion) do not know where to turn for dependable information.

There are several reasons why this field of knowledge has remained deplorably undeveloped. One is the simple matter of credibility. As mentioned above, when phenomena do not fit preconceived notions about the nature of things, many people, including many top-flight scientists, find it more comfortable to toss out the phenomena than to re-examine their preconceptions. Another reason for neglect is that the field unfortunately does attract charlatans, crackpots, and an earnest but uncritical fringe group. There has been a lot of chicanery in the past and an excess of naïveté. Consequently some of the solid scientific work has been discredited because of the instances in which, due to insufficient checks and controls, serious observers and investigators have been taken in. A third reason for neglect is the difficulty of replicability. Such phenomena cannot be reproduced upon command. They often fall to pieces under laboratory conditions even though they have been reliably observed in other situations. Among the chief characteristics of psi phenomena are their elusiveness, their illogicality, and their unpredictability.

But these days many of these deficiencies and excuses for neglect are being coped with. Out of their own experience scientists should know by now that it is the phenomena that *fail* to fit preconceived notions that are most deserving of further investigation. At its best the methodology of parapsychology now compares favorably with that of the natural sciences. In fact, parapsychologists have been under fire for so long that they know in advance exactly what criticisms to anticipate from their skeptical colleagues. And they go so far out of their way to structure their laboratory-type investigations and check their observations of spontaneous phenomena that their excessive precautions would be regarded as unnecessary if not ludicrous in the physical sciences. Being taken in by charlatanry and even by naïveté is now rarely a problem among experienced parapsychologists because they have learned what precautions to take to avoid being fooled.

Even the problem of replicability, perhaps the most justifiable of all the charges against parapsychology, is gradually coming under control. To cite one example only: some notable work is being done in telepathic communication between an agent (sender) and a sleeping subject, under laboratory conditions involving the most rigorous scientific methodology, utilizing electronic techniques (electroencephalograph) and elaborate devices for monitoring the procedures and evaluating the results (48). The experiments are too involved to report here beyond saying that results are proving dramatic to a degree, both when statistically analyzed and as reported anecdotally, and are being replicated elsewhere. That such work as this is being more and more accepted by orthodox science is evidenced by the growing demand for papers by professional journals and professional associations heretofore resistant to psychical research.

How does all this tie up with mental health education? Because it bears directly on our concepts of what human beings are like. If clairvoyance—the extrasensory perception of external events—exists (and it does), then what is the channel by which the events are cognized? If telepathy—extrasensory perception of the mental activities of another person—exists (and it does), then what is the relation of individual minds to each other and of each individual mind to what Aldous Huxley calls "mind at large"? If precognition—the cognition of a future event that could not be known through rational inference—exists (and it does), then what are the implications for our present ideas about cause and effect? From the point of view of logical positivism it is the last, precognition, that demands the most stretching of present day conceptual structures. How can events be known to human minds *before* they happen? But they are. So we simply have to reorder some of our most fundamental ideas about the nature of time and causality to make room for this phenomenon. A fascinating challenge to the Scientific Establishment.

COMPARATIVE RELIGION AND PHILOSOPHY

It is assuredly no coincidence that within the past decade or two both Existentialism and Zen Buddhism have become practically a "vogue" in this country and that in addition there has been a lively surge of interest in all the Eastern religions. More and more people, not only scholars and academicians but ordinary thinking people, are seeing that the East has something tremendously significant to offer the West, something particularly relevant to the cultural crisis of our period. It is beyond the scope of this chapter to try to analyze what it is that the West needs or can accept from the East except to speculate that perhaps the West is beginning to sense that the frenzied energy, the extroverted and materialistic goals that have made this country great now need the corrective of the more quiet, more passive, inward-turning, self-searching values of the East. Both Existentialism and Zen Buddhism, in their indefinable affinity, are in complete harmony with the basic orientation of the Third Force. All of them stress the importance of the direct experiencing of the present moment with definite controls set on the intrusion either of a no longer existent past or a not yet existent future; they stress the point of view that the individual *does* have choices, that he *is* responsible, and that he need *not* be the pawn of his own misperceptions; and they stress the opening of the self to full experience of the phenomenal world as an aspect of ultimate reality. If I were asked to point to *one* trend— only one—that I feel holds the most promise for the future of our culture I would say the coalescence of psychology and religion. But then I would have to hasten to clarify what I mean by psychology and what I mean by religion. By psychology I mean the humanistic goals of the Third Force as described above, recognizing that it is still too soon to know how effective they will finally prove to be and whether the leaders can remain true to their concepts, or whether some new series of weaknesses may arise as happened with the other two forces. By religion I mean what is sometimes called small-r religion: religion without creed or dogma or doctrine or ritual; religion that is concerned only with the individual's *direct personal experience,* as, for instance, William James delineated it in his epoch-making book *The Varieties of Religious Experience* (31).

The coalescence of psychology and religion in this sense implies the recognition of religious experience as proper subject matter for psychology, the recognition of psychology as a proper technique for the study of religious experience; and perhaps most important of all, an integration of the insights of the two fields.

It is significant that religion and philosophy, for so many centuries a foundation block of the humanistic tradition but long-divorced from science and psychology, are now being brought back into the fold as indicated by the very term "Humanistic Psychology." The implications for education are enormous. Perhaps the greatest of these is that a new and acceptable value is being placed on religious experience, particularly among those who are unwilling to subscribe to any specific set of beliefs and whose personal convictions and doubts place them outside organized religion, at least in part, even if they may conform outwardly. Under the new orientation young people will be encouraged not to hide or denigrate their higher experiences, but to cherish and cultivate them. Even certain words are being restored to their proper meaning. An outstanding example is mystic, mystical, mysticism, too often equated with "mysterious" or used pejoratively to suggest the merely vague or weirdo, but actually describing the highest form of inner subjective experience of which man is capable.

We have long had associations and journals and meetings devoted to "psychology and religion" that invariably turned out to be concerned with setting forth the psychiatric principles and techniques religious counselors ought to be familiar with. But now, under different names, we are getting associations and journals concerned with the psychological study of religious *experience*, which is very different indeed. We are also getting some bare beginnings of the development of techniques for the enhancement of religious experience such as the psychological study of meditation. And possibly most significant of all we are getting scientific recognition of the value of the religious experience by whatever name it is called and outside any theological framework.

EXPLORATIONS IN THE HUMAN POTENTIALITY

I never would have thought there could be any term more ambiguous than "mental health" but there is, and it is "human potentiality." Even so I find myself using the expression more and more, and I notice that its use seems to be growing. Like mental health it is a convenient term. Also like mental health, the word "movement" is being tagged on to it, as mentioned in an earlier section, and "the human potentiality movement" now has its devotees whose motivation reflects their Messianic ardor—which has both good and bad features.

I see the growing interest in the human potentiality not as a new philosophy because much of it is not new at all. Rather it is partly a rediscovery or restatement of long-established principles held in common by many of the traditional philosophies; partly a shift of emphasis from a limited and reductionist orientation to a broader and more inclusive one; and partly a natural extension of mental health concepts, just as mental health itself earlier reached out from treatment to prevention and thence to "positive" mental health.

Because of the ambiguity of the term human potentiality, it is necessary to set some limitations at the outset. Anything that is done for the benefit of any individual is an enhancement of his potential. I am not using the term as broadly as that here. I do not use it to refer to problems related to sickness, pathology, or deficiency; nor to efforts at increasing skills or efficiency through conditioning techniques, as in accelerated learning. Human potentiality as used here refers to the possibility for personal growth in the direction of high-level humanness, especially growth in those experiences, characteristics, and capacities that are uniquely human such as moral and spiritual development, insight into the understanding of self and others, and insight into the nature of reality.

Some of the current explorations in the non-cognitive dimensions of the human potentiality are proving extremely fruitful. Non-cognitive approaches to the study and enhancement of the human potentiality mean those emphases and techniques that attempt to bypass intellectualizing and conceptualizing ,processes and that center primarily on feeling, emotions, sensitivity and awareness, both sensory awareness and expanded or transcendent awareness.

The aspects of the human potentiality to be discussed here include:

- Congruences in intense subjective experiences
- Studies of peak experiences
- Meditation and control of brain waves
- Psychedelic drugs
- Hypnosis
- Sensitivity and awareness training

Congruences in Intense Subjective Experiences

Aldous Huxley was probably the first and certainly the most eloquent in pointing out certain congruences among four types of profound subjective experiences: the high-level creative experience; the religious mystical experience; the experience of some subjects under the influence of psychedelic drugs; and the subjective experiences of certain psychotic patients (29). To these four might also be added the experiences of sensitives, seers, and other persons gifted with ESP.

For example, a current study based on depth interviews with gifted artists cites instance after instance in which their own language describing their subjective state during the "white heat of creativeness" resembles the language of mystics throughout the ages (42). The same artists also reported a much larger percentage of experiences of extrasensory perception than would be expected in the general population. Their altered perceptions as they described them and as reflected in some of their productions resemble the altered perceptions reported by LSD and mescaline subjects, by subjects in certain types of hypnotic trance, and by occasional articulate schizophrenics. The insights of ancient seers, modern sensitives (28), and everyday people with occasional transcendental experiences show remarkable similarities as do many different types of experiences of extrasensory perception. The energy fields and vortices some sensitives are able to see and use in medical diagnoses (35) are consistent with the theoretical models of modern chemistry and mathematics, as well as with centuries-old occult lore. And so on. All such congruences are significant in studying the human potentiality and have not received a fraction of the attention they deserve.

Studies of Peak Experiences

Abraham Maslow has given us the useful term "peak experiences" to describe certain high-level subjective experiences. Maslow defines peak experiences as "secularized religious or mystical or transcendental experiences . . . the raw materials out of which not only religions can be built but also philosophies of any kind." I might add that not only world religions and classical philosophies but also personal religions and personal philosophies are built out of such experiences. They can be triggered by many types of life experiences and they occur in countless forms.

In general a peak experience is regarded by the individual as holding great value and significance for him. He often reports that these high moments have had lasting though perhaps indefinable after-effects, sometimes to the extent of having changed his life completely, in the manner of religious conversion or the types of conversion reported by Alcoholics Anonymous. He may feel an unshakable conviction that for a few instants he has been lifted to a higher plane of consciousness involving nonsensory perception and direct knowledge from which he has derived important new insights about himself or the universe or both. Other characteristics include an ineffable, often overwhelming sense of unity, oneness, identification, love, rightness, peace, truth—any degree and any combination of these or all of them. The experience of light is also a frequent characteristic. Such transcendental moments are usually brief in duration, sometimes lasting only seconds. Invariably the experience reflects a high moral tone and is often followed by a strong urge to impart the new insights for the benefit of others. All these are high levels of peak experiences, but the term is also useful in describing less exalted moments—Maslow speaks of "low peakers." Many, many people experience simpler forms of altered awareness and brief but poignant moments when fine emotions and insights flood the being—moments of joy, love, beauty, awe, insight, a sense of oneness with nature or ultimate reality or divinity, or however the individual chooses to express it.

The important thing to get across about peak experiences is that there are such things, that many people have them, and that they are greatly to be valued. Many young people will confess with satisfaction to having had such experiences but may never have discussed them for fear of being thought queer. Certainly such experiences are to be encouraged and developed for their contribution to personal development.

Meditation and Control of Brain Waves

The potential value of training in meditation has already been mentioned in the section on religion. Research emerging from psychiatric and psychological laboratories (27) is now confirming for Western culture what Eastern philosophical traditions have been teaching for centuries: that through various concentration and "inward turning" techniques, the individual may arrive at new levels of acceptance and peace. This is being further confirmed by newly developing techniques for training individuals in the conscious control of their brain waves, chiefly their alpha rhythms, a feat that until recently would not have been thought possible. Laboratory subjects who have succeeded in learning these techniques report the enhancement of a sense of serenity and certain ineffable gains in insight comparable to those experienced through successful meditative techniques (34).

Psychedelic Drugs

The psychedelic drug controversy has been only too well-aired in the mass media and is much too involved to go into here. Doubtless, argument will long continue to rage about the use of these drugs (LSD, mescaline, etc.) and the nature of the experience induced. A certain few facts can be definitively stated. It is incontrovertible that the drugs have been harmful to some people and that the hazard of their unsupervised use is great. Nevertheless it is also true that many people who have used them report profound, constructive, and lasting effects. Many describe their altered perceptions and consciousness in language dramatically similar to the reports of deep conversion and other religious experience, and claim that the insights they derive are greater than those experienced in other types of life situations, including prolonged psychoanalytic therapy. To speak of research in the psychedelic drugs as explorations in "inner space" comparable in significance to exploration in "outer space" is more than a play on words. The abuses of the psychedelics are a cause for deep concern and regret but so also are the restrictions on serious research. To deny scientists the right to explore these powerful mind-changing substances may deprive our culture of an exceptionally valuable technique for the enhancement of the human potential.

Hypnosis

Hypnosis is another of the research tools that has been explored amazingly little in relation to its known potential for constructive application. Some recent research is suggesting interesting new angles in the relation between concepts of time and changes in behavior, mood, and creativeness (26). When changes in time concepts (past, present, and future) are induced under hypnosis, corresponding changes in the subject's behavior range from behavior resembling the classical psychopathologies such as catatonic schizophrenia or depression to euphoric states; and striking variations in types of creative productions may be observed as well as altered perceptions comparable to other types of profound subjective experience.

Sensitivity and Awareness Training

Other techniques are being explored under such descriptive terms as sensitivity and awareness training, body awareness, sensory and kinesthetic training, fantasy and imagery training, research in 'the affective domain," "the new domain of the senses," "the noncognitive domain," and similar phrases.

The core of these innovative techniques is intensive attention to sensory awareness in the moment. Group methods are usual. They utilize a variety of techniques such as body movement and dance, contact with other bodies, concentration on body processes and inner states, multiple sensory stimuli, and the like. The purpose is to develop heightened awareness in the service of personal growth. The techniques often try to bypass specific individual problems instead of meeting them head on as in traditional psychotherapy. The groups frequently disclaim therapeutic intent or concern with "curing human sickness," preferring to place full emphasis on "improving human health." Participants often report increased creativeness and insight and a sense of more meaningful living.

Here then in all too small a nutshell I have tried to cram a multiplicity of impressions about some of today's shifting emphases: a broader, more sophisticated, more optimistic approach to the study of man, drawing on the lessons of pathology but focusing primarily on the dynamics of health and growth and normality; drawing also on the wisdom of other ages and other cultures; enlarging the concept of mental health to include a concept of the full human potential; and concerned particularly with the development of those moral and spiritual qualities in man that are uniquely human.

NEED FOR A NEW ETHIC

I have talked at length about the new psychology, changing concepts of the nature of man, the human potentiality as an extension of the mental health ideal, and burgeoning ideas in many areas. But in order to bring these into being as viable concepts useful to humanity it seems to me that there is one more thing we must have and that is a new ethic.

When I say "new" I do not mean literally new in the sense that it never existed before. What I am talking about has been there all the time. It is the oldest ethic in the world. But it does not seem to be thriving very well in recent decades. What seems to be called for now is a revitalization of a basic ethic relevant to the actions of men of good will everywhere.

Applied to the mental health effort such an ethic would take some very specific forms. In brief, we need an ethic:

— based on integrity and realism

— and on values other than those of the market place.

— Where intellectual dishonesty, however innocent and well-meaning, is unmasked

— and hypocrisy, whatever its guise, is recognized for what it is.

— Where education does not mean "selling"

— and communication does not mean "getting somebody to do what you want them to do."

— Where the motivation for research is curiosity and a passion for truth, not the renewal of a government grant or getting one's name on the program of a professional meeting or a raise in salary.

— Where the "pursuit of excellence" becomes an end in itself

— and a job well done carries its own reward in satisfaction regardless of any other gains.

— Where a man's creativeness is judged not by his cleverness in tearing down, but by his skill in building up.

— Where concern for "the welfare of mankind" is neither corny nor pie-in-the-sky idealism

— and "caring" is regarded as a value.

— Where a concept of service is respected and encouraged as a laudable life goal and instilled into our young people.

— And where responsibility is regarded as a solemn moral obligation in all walks of life.

Acknowledgments

First, I wish to thank my colleagues Alex Sareyan and Jack Neher at the Mental Health Materials Center for their deft management of the seminars. To all the seminar participants, I express my appreciation for our friendly and stimulating interchanges. I am grateful to the several people who criticized the manuscript and wish I could mention them all. Two who were outstandingly helpful were Sylvan S. Furman, Assistant Commissioner, New York State Department of Mental Hygiene, who shared with me some of his thoughtful convictions about community mental health; and Abraham H. Maslow, of Brandeis University, who gave me the courage to say what I wanted to say in the last chapter. My secretary, Mrs. Dorothy Reisman, warmed me with her unflagging interest. And my husband, Max Boll, as always with any effort of mine, made the whole thing possible.

Nina Ridenour
February 2, 1968

List of Seminars on

"THE SKILLFUL USE OF

MENTAL HEALTH MATERIALS"

December, 1964   New York City.

January, 1965   Chapel Hill, North Carolina. Co-sponsored by the School of Public Health, University of North Carolina, and the North Carolina Department of Mental Health.

March, 1965   Los Angeles, California. Co-sponsored by the Department of Psychiatry, University of California Medical School, and the California Department of Mental Hygiene.

September, 1965   St. Louis, Missouri. Sponsored by the Department of Neurology and Psychiatry, St. Louis University.

January, 1966   New Orleans, Louisiana. Co-sponsored by the Department of Psychiatry, Tulane University School of Medicine; the Louisiana State Board of Health; and the Louisiana Association for Mental Health.

June, 1966   Baltimore, Maryland. Co-sponsored by Johns Hopkins University School of Hygiene and Public Health and the Society of Public Health Educators.

The seminars were attended by a total of 103 participants.

List of Guest Lecturers

Vera Allen—Actress and Board Member, Plays for Living

Edward Auer, M.D.—Chairman, Department of Psychiatry, St. Louis University School of Medicine

Ralph Boatman, Ph.D.—Chairman, Department of Health Education, School of Public Health, University of North Carolina

Dorothy Bradbury—Director, Division of Publications, Children's Bureau, Department of Health, Education, and Welfare

Norman Brill, M.D.—Chairman, Department of Psychiatry, Medical School, University of California at Los Angeles

Orville Brim, Ph.D.—President, Russell Sage Foundation

Julien Bryan—Documentary Film Producer and President, International Film Foundation

Robert Dahl—Public Information Officer, Illinois Department of Mental Health

Nicholas Dallis, M.D.—Psychiatrist, Creator of "Rex Morgan, M.D."

W. Gerald Davenport—Social Work Consultant, New York City Mission Society

Rudolf Flesch, Ph.D.—Lecturer and Author of *How to Speak, Write, and Think More Effectively*

Harold Halpert—Consultant on Communications, Research Utilization Branch, National Institute of Mental Health

Lura Jackson—Chief, Public Information Branch, National Institute of Mental Health

Frances Jordan—Family Relations Specialist, Agricultural Extension Service, North Carolina State College

Miriam Karlins—Coordinator of Volunteer and Educational Services, Minnesota Department of Welfare

Rosemary Kent, Ph.D.—Faculty, University of North Carolina School of Public Health

Milton Kossack—Director of Health Education, Louisiana State Board of Health

Lawrence S. Kubie, M.D.—Consultant in Training and Research, Sheppard and Enoch Pratt Hospital

Paul Lemkau, M.D.—Professor of Mental Hygiene, Johns Hopkins University School of Hygiene and Public Health

Israel Light, Ph.D.—Project Officer, National Clearinghouse for Mental Health Information, National Institute of Mental Health

William Mason, M.D.—Chief Health Educator, Georgia Department of Public Health

Esther Middlewood—Director of Mental Health Education, Michigan Department of Mental Health

Joseph Musial—Free-lance Cartoonist and formerly Director of Education, King Features, Inc.

Margaret Oliver—Program Leader, Division of Home Economics, Federal Extension Service, U.S. Department of Agriculture

Lucile Pepoon—Family Life Specialist, Cooperative Extension Service, University of Illinois

Loyd W. Rowland, Ph.D.—Author and Education Consultant, Louisiana Association for Mental Health

Nora Stirling—Author and Playwright

Hiawatha Walker, Ph.D.—Faculty, University of North Carolina School of Public Health

Rev. Dr. Harold Wilke—Director, Council for Church and Ministry, United Church of Christ

(The above identifications represent the positions held by the guest lecturers at the time of the seminars, not necessarily their present posts.)

References

BOOKS

1. Bowlby, John. *Maternal Care and Mental Health*. Geneva: World Health Organization (WHO), 1952. (Distributed by Columbia University Press)
2. Caplan, Gerald. *Principles of Preventive Psychiatry*. New York: Basic Books, 1964.
3. (Cornell Conference Report.) *Mental Health Education: A Critique*. Philadelphia: Pennsylvania Mental Health, 1960.
4. Elinson, Jack, et al. *Public Image of Mental Health Services*. Report of a Joint Project of the Columbia University School of Public Health and Administrative Medicine and the New York City Community Mental Health Board. New York: Mental Health Materials Center, 1967.
5. Ginsburg, Sol W. *A Psychiatrist's Views on Social Issues*. New York: Columbia University Press, 1963.
6. Hoffman, Martin L., and Lois W. Hoffman, eds. *Review of Child Development Research*, 2v. New York: Russell Sage Foundation, 1964, 1966.

7. Jahoda, Marie. *Current Concepts of Positive Mental Health.* (A report of the Joint Commission on Mental Illness and Health.) New York: Basic Books, 1958.

8. Joint Commission on Mental Health and Illness. *Action for Mental Health.* Final Report of the Commission. New York: Basic Books, 1961.

9. Ridenour, Nina. *Mental Health in the United States: A Fifty-Year History.* Cambridge: Harvard University Press, 1961. (Published by the Press for the Commonwealth Fund)

10. (Swampscott Conference Report.) *Psychiatry, the Press, and the Public: Problems in Communication.* Washington: American Psychiatric Association, 1956.

PROGRAM MATERIALS *(Books, pamphlets, plays, leaflets, films)*

11. *Blondie* (Mental Health Comic Book). Illustrated by Joe Musial. Albany: New York State Department of Mental Hygiene, 1950.

12. Children's Bureau. *Infant Care.* Washington, D.C.: The Bureau, Department of Health, Education and Welfare, 1963. (First published in 1914)

13. Group for the Advancement of Psychiatry (GAP). *Emotional Aspects of School Desegregation,* Report No. 37A, March, 1960. (Abbreviated version of *Psychiatric Aspects of School Desegregation,* Report No. 37, May, 1957.) New York: Group for the Advancement of Psychiatry.

14. ———. *Mental Retardation: A Family Crisis—The Therapeutic Role of the Physician,* Report No. 56, December, 1963. New York: Group for the Advancement of Psychiatry.

15. Kelly, Walt. *Pogo Primer for Parents (TV Division).* Washington, D.C.: Children's Bureau, Department of Health, Education and Welfare, 1961.

16. Menninger, William C. *Seven Keys to a Happy Life.* Chicago: National Research Bureau, 1963. (Original title: *Seven Criteria of Emotional Maturity*)

17. National Association for Mental Health. *Mental Health Is . . . 1,2,3.* New York: the Association, 1951.

18. *Plays for Living.* Published by Plays for Living, a division of the Family Service Association of America, New York.

19. Redlich, Fritz, and June Bingham. *The Inside Story: Psychiatry and Everyday Life.* New York: Vintage Books, 1953. (Paperback, Vintage, 1960)

20. Ridenour, Nina, and Isabel Johnson. *Some Special Problems of Children: Aged Two to Five Years.* New York: Child Study Association of America, 1966. (First published in 1947 by the New York City Committee on Mental Hygiene)

21. Rowland, Loyd W. *Pierre the Pelican.* (Letters for Young Parents.) New Orleans: Louisiana Association for Mental Health, 1947, 1957.

22. ———. et al. *Milestones to Maturity.* New Orleans: Louisiana Association for Mental Health, 1951, 1962.

23. ———. Police Training Films: *Booked for Safekeeping, The Cry for Help, The Mask, Under Pressure.* (Available from National Medical Audiovisual Center, Chamblee, Georgia 30005)

24. Stern, Edith M. *Mental Illness: A Guide for the Family.* New York: National Association for Mental Health, 1968.

25. Stirling, Nora, and Nina Ridenour. *My Name Is Legion* (A dramatization of the life of Clifford W. Beers). New York: National Association for Mental Health, 1953.

SELECTED REFERENCES PERTAINING TO THE
HUMAN POTENTIALITY

26. Aaronson, Bernard S. "Behavior and the Place Names of Time," *American Journal of Hypnosis,* 9, July, 1966. (Also many other articles on hypnosis and concepts of time by Aaronson)

27. Deikman, Arthur J. "Experimental Meditation," *Journal of Nervous and Mental Disease,* 136, April, 1963.

28. Garrett, Eileen J. *Awareness.* New York: Garrett Publications, 1943.

29. Huxley, Aldous. *The Doors of Perception,* 1954, and *Heaven and Hell,* 1955. New York: Harper and Brothers. Both titles reissued in one-volume paperback, 1963, and hardcover, 1964. New York: Harper and Row.

30. ———. *The Perennial Philosophy.* New York: Harper and Brothers, 1945. (Paperback, Meridian, 1962)

31. James, William. *The Varieties of Religious Experience.* New York: Random House, Modern Library, 1936. (First published in 1902)

32. Johnson, Raynor C. *The Imprisoned Splendour: An Approach to Reality Based Upon Significant Data Drawn from the Fields of Natural Science, Psychical Research, and Mystical Experience.* New York: Harper and Row, 1954.

33. Jung, C. G. *Memories, Dreams, Reflections.* Recorded and edited by Aniela Jaffe. New York: Pantheon Books, 1963. (Paperback, Vintage, 1965)

34. Kamiya, Joseph. "Conscious Control of Brain Waves." *Psychology Today*, April, 1968.

35. Karagulla, Shafica. *Breakthrough to Creativity: Your Higher Sense Perception.* Los Angeles: De Vorss, 1967.

36. Laski, Marghanita. *Ecstasy: A Study in Some Secular and Religious Experiences.* Bloomington: Indiana University Press, 1962.

37. Maslow, Abraham H. *Motivation and Personality.* New York: Harper and Row, 1954.

38. ———. *Toward a Psychology of Being.* New York: Van Nostrand, 1962.

39. ———. *Religions, Values, and Peak-Experiences.* Columbus: Ohio State University Press, 1964.

40. ———. *The Psychology of Science: A Reconnaissance.* New York: Harper and Row, 1966.

41. Murphy, Gardner, and Robert O. Ballou. *William James on Psychical Research.* New York: Viking, 1960.

42. Osis, Karlis. Unpublished manuscript on creativity and extrasensory perception.

43. Pratt, J. Gaither. *Parapsychology: An Insider's View.* New York: Doubleday, 1964.

44. Rhine, Louisa E. *Hidden Channels of the Mind.* New York: William Sloane Associates, 1961. (Paperback, Apollo)

45. Rogers, Carl. "Towards a Science of the Person," *Journal of Humanistic Psychology*, Fall 1963.

46. Stace, W. T. *Mysticism and Philosophy.* Philadelphia: Lippincott, 1960.

47. ———. *Religion and the Modern Mind.* Philadelphia: Lippincott, 1952, 1960.

48. Ullman, Montague. "An Experimental Approach to Dreams and Telepathy: Methodology and Preliminary Findings," *Archives of General Psychiatry*, June, 1966. (Also many other articles in psychiatric and psychological journals by Ullman and his associate, Stanley Krippner, describing research at Maimonides Hospital, Brooklyn, N.Y.)